# THE SYMPHONIES FOR ORGAN

## Symphonie II

# RECENT RESEARCHES IN THE MUSIC OF THE NINETEENTH AND EARLY TWENTIETH CENTURIES

*Rufus Hallmark and D. Kern Holoman, general editor*

---

A-R Editions, Inc., publishes seven series of musicological editions
that present music brought to light in the course of current research:

*Recent Researches in the Music of the Middle Ages and Early Renaissance*
Charles Atkinson, general editor

*Recent Researches in the Music of the Renaissance*
James Haar, general editor

*Recent Researches in the Music of the Baroque Era*
Christoph Wolff, general editor

*Recent Researches in the Music of the Classical Era*
Eugene K. Wolf, general editor

*Recent Researches in the Music of the Nineteenth and Early Twentieth Centuries*
Rufus Hallmark and D. Kern Holoman, general editors

*Recent Researches in American Music*
H. Wiley Hitchcock, general editor

*Recent Researches in the Oral Traditions of Music*
Philip V. Bohlman, general editor

Each *Recent Researches* edition is devoted to works
by a single composer or to a single genre of composition.
The contents are chosen for their potential interest to scholars
and performers, then prepared for publication according to the
standards that govern the making of all reliable historical editions.

Subscribers to any of these series, as well as patrons of subscribing institutions,
are invited to apply for information about the "Copyright-Sharing Policy"
of A-R Editions, Inc., under which policy any part of an edition
may be reproduced free of charge for study or performance.

For information contact

A-R EDITIONS, INC.
801 Deming Way
Madison, Wisconsin 53717

(608) 836-9000

RECENT RESEARCHES IN THE MUSIC OF THE NINETEENTH
AND EARLY TWENTIETH CENTURIES • VOLUME 12

Charles-Marie Widor

# THE SYMPHONIES FOR ORGAN

## Symphonie II

Edited by John R. Near

A-R Editions, Inc.
Madison

Charles-Marie Widor
THE SYMPHONIES FOR ORGAN

Edited by John R. Near

*Recent Researches in the Music
of the Nineteenth and Early Twentieth Centuries*

| Opus 13 | Symphonie I   | in C Minor | Volume 11 |
|---------|---------------|------------|-----------|
|         | Symphonie II  | in D Major | Volume 12 |
|         | Symphonie III | in E Minor | Volume 13 |
|         | Symphonie IV  | in F Minor | Volume 14 |
| Opus 42 | Symphonie V    | in F Minor | Volume 15 |
|         | Symphonie VI   | in G Minor | Volume 16 |
|         | Symphonie VII  | in A Minor | Volume 17 |
|         | Symphonie VIII | in B Major | Volume 18 |
| Opus 70 | *Symphonie gothique* | | Volume 19 |
| Opus 73 | *Symphonie romane*   | | Volume 20 |

© 1991 by A-R Editions, Inc.
All rights reserved
Printed in the United States of America

*Library of Congress Cataloging-in-Publication Data*

Widor, Charles-Marie, 1844–1937.
Symphonie II.

  (The symphonies for organ / Charles-Marie Widor)
(Recent researches in the music of the nineteenth and
early twentieth centuries, ISSN 0193-5364 ; v. 11)
  Includes critical commentary and bibliographical
references.
  1. Symphonies (Organ). I. Near, John Richard,
1947– . II. Series: Widor, Charles-Marie,
1844–1937. Symphonies, organ (A-R Editions).
III. Series: Recent researches in the music of the
nineteenth and early twentieth centuries ; v. 11)
M2.R23834 vol. 11[M8]         90-753022
ISBN 0-89579-250-8

# Contents

Introduction
   The Sources    vii
   Editorial Policies    viii
   Widor's Registrations    viii
   Critical Commentary    ix

Widor's *Avant-propos*    xiv

Symphonie II in D Major
   I. Praeludium Circulare    3
   II. Pastorale    8
   III    15
   IV. Salve Regina    24
   V. Adagio    31
   VI. Finale    35

Appendix 1
   [I] Prélude. Version *A/A'*    43

Appendix 2
   I. Prélude. Version *B/B'*, Mm. 19–28, 54–100    48

Appendix 3
   III. Versions *A'/B/B'* and *C/C'*, Mm. 1–44    51

Appendix 4
   IV. Scherzo. Version *A/A'/B/B'*    53

Appendix 5
   [V] Adagio. Version *A/A'*    59

Unsigned oil painting of Widor, dated 1874 on the wooden canvas stretcher
Courtesy of the Widor family

# Introduction

From the time of their first publication, the organ symphonies of Charles-Marie Widor (1844–1937) have been recognized as masterpieces. Their influence on subsequent organ literature was once immense. As new generations of organ music became popular, however, there inevitably came a time when Widor's symphonies were neglected, often being judged outmoded. Even the French Romantic organ, perfected by Cavaillé-Coll and adored by musicians, was abused by later generations. Sufficient time was required to pass before Widor's art and instrument could be considered from a fresh and independent musical perspective. That perspective has evidently been achieved, for in recent years increasing numbers of musicians have begun evaluating the symphonies on their own terms, with the result that the works have enjoyed a notable resurgence of popularity. At the same time, the French Romantic organ has regained its former status.

Widor was perhaps his own most demanding critic. Following the first publication of each organ symphony, a continual transformation was effected by the composer through several revisions. In certain cases nearly six decades intervened between first and last versions of a work. Even after the final published edition, Widor continued to scrutinize his organ works, applying finishing touches to the pieces that have constituted his most enduring legacy.

This comprehensive edition of Widor's ten organ symphonies is the first to incorporate the many final emendations made by the composer in his own copies. Here also are presented for the first time together substantially or completely different earlier versions of passages, sections, and complete movements as they were conceived by Widor in the course of his long career. Using information in the Critical Commentary and the music of the Appendixes, musicians can perform or study these several earlier versions of each work.

The Preface to this edition (vol. 11, Symphonie I) provides a full discussion of the symphonies' genesis and historical environment as well as an extended discussion of editorial policy, sources, and performance. In this Introduction are provided information on performance sufficient to give the reader a sense of Widor's own preferences in registration and expression (including a translation of his foreword, or *avant-propos*), a conspectus of the sources, a summary of editorial policy, and a Critical Commentary.

## The Sources

The original French editions and copies of these with corrections and emendations in Widor's hand form the basis for this critical edition. The locations of Widor's original holographs, if extant, are unknown. After extensively researching these works, the editor believes that all editions have surfaced, with one possible exception, noted in the Preface. These are listed here together with the identifying abbreviations used in the Critical Commentary and Appendixes. (More complete information on the sources appears in the Preface to the present edition.)

*A*  The first edition of opus 13, Symphonies I–IV, published in Paris in 1872 by the firm of J. Maho.

*A'*  A subsequent issue of *A* with minuscule alterations, published in 1879 by the firm of J. Hamelle together with the first editions of Symphonies V and VI.

*B*  The first complete issue of opus 42, comprising Symphonies V–VIII, together with the first major revision of opus 13, published in Paris in 1887 by Hamelle.

*B'*  A subsequent issue of *B* with small revisions to Symphonies I, VI, VII, and VIII, released between 1888 and 1892.

*C*  A new edition of opuses 13 and 42 (excepting Symphonie VI), published in 1901 and bearing the heading "New edition, revised, and entirely modified by the composer (1900–1901)."

*C'*  A subsequent issue of *C* that includes a new version of Symphonie VI and revisions to Symphonies I–V and VII–VIII, released by 1911.

*D*  A new edition of opuses 13 and 42, published in 1920, bearing the heading "New edition, revised, and entirely modified by the composer (1914–1918), (1920)."

*E*  The final published edition, again with revisions, issued 1928–29.

*Emend 1*  A copy of *B'* apparently used by Widor while preparing the revisions of edition *C* but also containing other emendations.

*Emend 2*  A bound and complete collection of single symphonies (representing variously the versions of editions *D* or *E*) with emendations made by Widor mostly after 1929, the year of edition *E*.

*Emend 3*  A copy of Symphonie V in the version of edition *D*, with numerous emendations by the composer, dated October 1927 in Widor's hand. This copy includes the revisions present in the 1929 edition, but it also contains further emendations, including some duplicated in *Emend* 2 and arguably entered after 1929.

Identical versions of movements in different editions are denoted in the Critical Commentary and the Appendixes by a slash between the identifying letters; for example, *A/A'/B/B'* means that a movement so identified remains the same through editions *A*, *A'*, *B*, and *B'*.

## Editorial Policies

Edition *E* (or, what amounts to the same thing, a version remaining constant through edition *E*) is generally taken as the principal source for the main body of this edition. Sources for Appendix variants are identified individually in the Critical Commentary. All departures from the source either are distinguished typographically (when they are editorial and straightforward) or are identified in the Critical Commentary (when they derive from other sources or are not explained by policies described here). There are two exceptions to the policy of bracketing: editorial ties, slurs, hairpins, and directs are dashed; editorial cautionary accidentals appear in reduced size; all other editorial additions are enclosed in brackets.

The original French prints are themselves replete with cautionary accidentals, usually provided to cancel flats and sharps in previous measures. All except repetitious cautionary accidentals within a measure are preserved in this edition.

In the Critical Commentary the three staves of a system are indexed 1, 2, and 3, in order from top to bottom. Occasionally staff 1 in the source editions is congested, while an empty or nearly empty staff lies directly below. In such contexts this edition sometimes tacitly transfers left-hand voices to the open staff 2.

In the sources, indications of dynamics under staff 1 are sometimes duplicated under staves 2 or 3 or both in contexts where the Pédale and other manuals would have to share those dynamics in any event. The editor has suppressed most of these redundant dynamic indications. In addition, the old engravings frequently place dynamic indications over staff 1 because of space limitations on the page; conversely, they sometimes place tempo indications between staves 1 and 2 for the same reason. This edition tacitly regularizes the position of all such marks, putting dynamic indications within the system and tempo indications above it. There is an obvious exception to this rule: namely, when a dynamic is meant to apply to one staff alone, it appears closest to the affected voice(s)—therefore, sometimes above staff 1. Because Widor indicated registration and dynamics somewhat differently in editions *A* and *A'*, the source placement of the relevant signs is preserved in appendix extracts from them.

Widor indicated staccato with the dot up to the late 1890s, but he favored the wedge thereafter. The two signs become mixed in passages partially revised by the composer after about 1900 (the period of edition *C*). Widor's pedagogical works on organ music reveal that both signs had the same significance for him. In the present edition all wedges are tacitly changed to dots in pieces conceived before Widor's change of orthography; wedges are retained in movements composed after the change.

Beaming in the original French editions is sometimes used to clarify phrasing. Beaming in the new edition follows that of the sources except when, under certain stringent conditions spelled out in detail in the Preface to this edition (see vol. 11, *Symphonie I*), it can be shown with great probability that inconsistencies arise through oversight or through adherence to an outmoded convention for beaming.

Characteristic of Widor's musical orthography is its attention to inner contrapuntal voices in every musical texture. At times this leads to a phalanx of stems all aiming for the same metrical position. Stemming in the new edition generally follows that of the sources, since the appearance of counterpoint, even in predominantly homophonic textures, conveys much of the "feel" and attitude proper to Widor's symphonies. Departures from the source are made only in clearly defined circumstances spelled out in detail in the Preface to this edition. In general, the number of voices in a measure is kept constant. In clearly homophonic contexts, where Widor himself is less strict, inconsistencies in the number of voices in a measure are usually allowed to stand. All editorial rests are bracketed. Stems added by analogy with parallel or closely similar passages are not bracketed, but the source reading is reported in a critical note. All other stems added to clarify inconsistent voicing are bracketed. Infrequently, superfluous rests or stems in the sources are tacitly removed to keep part writing consistent in a measure.

In conformity with accepted practice of that era, the original French editions of Widor's organ symphonies provide double barlines for all changes of key and for some changes of meter. In this edition these are converted to single barlines unless there is also a new tempo, a new texture, or some other sign of a structural subdivision.

Reference to pitch in the Critical Commentary is made as follows: middle $C = c'$; C above middle $C = c''$; C below middle $C = c$; two octaves below middle $C = C$. Successive pitches are separated by commas, simultaneous pitches by virgules.

## Widor's Registrations

Widor generally indicated registrations by family of tone-color instead of exact stop nomenclature. In so doing he never intended to condone willful or indiscriminate interpretations of his registrational plans. He had a particular horror of kaleidoscopic stop changes and artlessly haphazard use of the Expression pedal. To those who indulged in a continual manipulation of the stops or Expression pedal, he habitually advised, "I beg you, no magic lantern effects." Barring the unfortunate necessity of making certain adaptations to varying organs, one should no more alter the "orchestration" of a Widor organ symphony than change or dress up the instrumentation of a Beethoven symphony. Clearly, the faithful realization of Widor's registrational plan is essential to the presentation of these works as the composer heard them. Beyond this, knowledge of the Cavaillé-Coll organ, the instrument preferred by Widor, will also prove useful to the performer intent on maximum fidelity to the composer's intention. A discussion of this organ and its constraints on performance can be found in the Preface to this edition (see vol. 11, Symphonie I).

To indicate the registration he wanted, Widor adopted a relatively simple shorthand system: **G** represents Grand-orgue (Great); **P** Positif (Positive); **R** Récit (Swell); **Péd.** Pédale (Pedal). Fonds are the foundation stops; Anches the chorus reed stops as well as all correlative stops included in the Jeux de combinaison. Pitch designations are self-evident.

When found above, within, or directly below the keyboard staves, a single letter instructs the organist to play on that particular uncoupled manual. When two or three letters are combined in these locations, the first designates the manual to play on, the second and subsequent letters what is to be coupled to it. For example, **GPR** instructs the organist to play on the Grand-orgue with the Positif and Récit coupled to it; **PR** tells one to play on the Positif with the Récit coupled to it; and so on.

When found under the lowest staff, one or more letters designate which manuals are to be coupled to the Pédale. When Widor employs only a dynamic marking in the course of the Pédale line, the performer should determine at his own discretion which Pédale coupler needs to be retired or reintroduced.

All crescendo and decrescendo indications, no matter how lengthy, are to be effected only by manipulation of the Expression pedal, unless the crescendo leads to a *fff*. In that case the Jeux de combinaison of each division are to be brought into play successively on strong beats: first those of the Récit (perhaps already on), then those of the Positif (sometimes indicated with a *ff*), and finally those of the Grand-orgue and Pédale on the *fff*. For the decrescendo they are to be retired in reverse order on weak beats.

## Critical Commentary

Versions *A*, *A'*, *B/B'*, *C*, *C'*, *D*, and *E* provide variant readings of this symphony that differ from as little as two notes to as much as an entire movement. In its original form the symphony is stylistically homogeneous. With the interpolation of the Salve Regina, conceived nearly thirty years later, Widor juxtaposed a style radically different from the older, surrounding movements. This is the only brand-new movement—one not rooted in an earlier composition—added as late as edition C. Although an exceptional work in its own right, it brings a certain weightiness previously not present in the symphony.

Admirable in Symphonie II is its deployment of tone color. Widor seems to be taking the listener on a timbral tour of the organ. Each successive movement features fresh combinations, as illustrated by the registrational scheme of the original version: I. Fonds 8'; II. Fonds 16', 8', 4', Hautbois melody with accompanying Flûtes 8', Hautbois, Clarinette, and Flûtes 16', 8' in trio; III. Fonds 8', Voix célestes, Flûtes 8', 4'; IV. Anches 8', 4'; V. Voix humaines; VI. Tutti. The Salve Regina similarly introduces new tone colors with its registration of (Fonds 8', 4' and) Mixtures, Fonds 8', Flûtes 8', 4', Trompette cantus firmus.

Symphonie II has no formally contrapuntal movements such as the Prélude and fugal Finale of Symphonie I. Nevertheless, counterpoint is virtually always present in the musical texture, exemplifying Widor's statement that he tried to make pieces which, while being free, feature some contrapuntal procedures (see p. xxi of the Preface to this edition, found in vol. 11, Symphonie I).

### I. Praeludium Circulare

This movement was published in five different versions: *A/A'*, *B/B'*, *C*, *C'*, and *D/E*. Titled simply "Prélude" until edition C, it was renamed "Praeludium Circulare" to reflect the modulatory explorations of the movement. Between the opening and close in D major, the piece touches harmonically upon all twelve degrees of the chromatic scale. In this way Widor continues a tradition among organists that begins no later than Spinacino's "Recercar de tutti li toni" of 1507 and that continues through Beethoven's two preludes through all twelve keys, opus 39.

While the five versions of this movement are obviously related, Widor's revisions brought about some dramatic changes. All versions are similar until measure 38. From that point *A/A'* and *B/B'* are related until measure 64, where *B/B'* becomes more expansive, replacing thirteen measures of *A/A'* with thirty new measures. Both versions then end with the same seven measures. Editions *C* and *C'* are closely related; *C'* has modifications only in measures 55–56; besides this, it only supplies four missing accidentals. Edition *C'* and version *D/E* are also closely related, the main modifications appearing in measures 42–52, 55, 58–59, and from 65 to the end. Version *B/B'* is completely different from version *D/E* after measure 37. In the editor's view, *B/B'* is as musically convincing as *D/E*; the player may, in fact, find that its style is more cohesive. Passages unique to version *B/B'* are given in Appendix 2. To facilitate further comparisons with *B/B'*, version *A/A'* is given in Appendix 1. For the final version, edition *E* is the principal source.

CRITICAL NOTES

M. 11, staff 1, upper voice, note 5 is g'-natural in A/A' and B/B'—the accidental was evidently deleted when the measure was revised in C; see the analogous melodic motive in m. 3 and the discussion for the same motive in m. 42. M. 39, staff 1, upper voice, note 2 has no eighth flag. M. 42, staff 2, upper voice, note 4 has no accidental—edition follows *Emend* 2; staff 3, the measure is metrically incomplete—note 1 needs either a dot or a subsequent eighth rest; the edition takes the latter option in order to coordinate with the rhythmically related lower voice in staff 2 (in C and C' note 1 is dotted—when the measure was revised for edition D the dot was deleted, either by error or to allow an eighth rest that somehow did not get engraved). M. 43, staff 2, beat 1, grace notes engraved before bar line—throughout the ten symphonies the usual practice is to place grace notes (as opposed to *Nachschlag*s) after the bar line. M. 48, staff 2, upper voice, note 2 has no eighth flag. M. 56, staff 1, lower voice, note 5 is tied to next measure in C and C'—the tie was probably omitted by error when the measure was reengraved for edition D. M. 57, staff 1, beat 2, enigmatic eighth rest near f'-sharp. M. 67, staff 1, upper voice, note 5, see discussion for m. 11. M. 73, staff 1, upper voice, beat 3 has a' quarter note (beat 4 is empty)—editorial half note and tie follow C and C'. M. 77, staff 2, lower voice, note 1 has no dot.

*II. Pastorale*

In ternary form, this movement is replete with grace and aural color. It is also noteworthy for its fresh rhythmic ideas, its juxtaposition of legato melody with staccato accompaniment, and its deft imitative writing in the middle section. The movement remained largely unchanged after its inception. A few minuscule modifications permit us to define three similar versions: A/A'/B/B', C/C'/D, and E. Edition E is the principal source.

CRITICAL NOTES

M. 10, staff 2, lower voice, note 1 has enigmatic slur or tie to next measure—edition follows analogous m. 68. M. 18, staff 3, note 3 has staccato dot in all editions—this is incongruous with the note value. M. 19, this is one of the rare times that Widor calls for an enclosed Positif—note the louder dynamic in m. 22. M. 22, staff 1, upper voice, the final tie follows editions A through D—it undoubtedly faded from the source plate, a probable vestige of it being visible in primary sets 1 and 2 of E. M. 24, beat 2, *agitato* is above staff 1 in editions B through D—its absence here is likely the result of deterioration in the plate—see the critical note for movement III, m. 53. M. 42, *pp* is in front of brace with no manual indication in all editions. M. 52, staff 1, note 5 appears to have staccato dot beginning in edition B—the dot is likely an erroneous spot on the plate (it is not centered under the note, and it is not contextually congruous). M. 66, staff 2, dyad 8, lower note is c'-sharp in all editions—edition follows *Emend* 2 and analogous m. 8; beat 4, the sharp is correspondingly moved to c'. M. 85, staff 1, manual changes not in any edition—edition follows *Emend* 2. M. 97, staff 1, grace notes engraved before bar line in all editions—see report for movement 1, m. 43; staves 2 and 3, beat 2 has quarter rest, eighth rest in A/A'/B/B' and C/C'/D.

*III*

Widor utilizes a wealth of compositional ideas in this piece. Choralelike textures (at the opening) and fanciful arabesques (beginning at m. 23) lead to a rhapsodic middle section (mm. 53ff.) constructed of bits of imitation and sequence, the whole intensified by repetition a half step higher (mm. 76ff.). After the return to the opening idea (m. 95), themes are masterfully juxtaposed and developed. A lovely Flûte melody soars over sustained chords at the end.

The movement has four versions: A, A'/B/B', C/C', and D/E. In edition A' Widor corrected two minor faults in the part writing of edition A. Version D/E is seven measures shorter than earlier ones, though all versions are nearly identical after measure 36 of D/E. The different registrational color and, in the variant portion, compositional style of versions A'/B/B' and C/C' are very effective. Measures 1–44 of these are given in Appendix 3. For the final version, edition E is the principal source.

Paris, Bibliothèque nationale, Ms 18135, is an autograph score comprising the second and third movements of a *Symphonie d'orgue* for organ and orchestra ("Opus 42"), dated by the composer "3 avril 82" at the end of the third movement (p. 76). The second movement, found on pages 31–39 of the autograph, presents the musical materials of Symphonie II, movement III, version A'/B/B', redistributed for organ and string orchestra.*

CRITICAL NOTES

M. 22, staff 1, lower voice, note 2 has no eighth flag. M. 41, staff 1, beat 3, sharp is on c" (already sharp from beat 1) instead of f". M. 53, editorial *agitato* follows editions B through D—the *agitato* is nearly faded in D, so its absence in E is probably due to further deterioration in the plate; the hypothesis of plate deterioration (as opposed to authorial intent) is supported by three facts: a return to *tempo primo* remains at m. 72; an *agitato* is present at m. 76; and no *agitato* has been marked for deletion in *Emend* 2. M. 74, staff 2, beat 1, g has stem up and f has stem down—this results in faulty part writing. M. 82, staff 3, note 2 is B-sharp in all editions—when the analogous note in m. 59 was revised from B-natural to G (in edition C), the corresponding revision from B-sharp to G-sharp was not carried out in m. 82; edition follows *Emend* 2, where Widor clearly marks "sol" in the margin but then incorrectly places a dagger over note 2 of m. 83 instead of m. 82.

---

*This manuscript together with the associated manuscript Paris, Bibliothèque nationale, Vma Ms 603 (where the work is entitled *Symphonie pour orgue et orchestre*), are further described in the introduction to Symphonie VI.

M. 108, staves 1 and 2, braced manual directive **P** is confirmed by editions *A* and *A'*, which have a brace in m. 106—the brace was inadvertently removed when the registrational nomenclature was changed for edition *B*; staff 2, editorial tie appears as in editions *A* and *A'*. M. 132, staves 1 and 2, manual directive is smudged **R** in source; **P** appears in many prints—the subsequent decrescendo hairpin and change of manual to **P** at m. 143 confirm **R**.

## IV. *Salve Regina*

The Salve Regina, a chorale fantasy based on the well-known Gregorian antiphon for the Blessed Virgin Mary, replaces (beginning with edition *C*) the original Scherzo. It is a product of Widor's last style period, during which he often drew on plainsong for melodic material. Even the freely composed accompanying lines frequently take on the melismatic fluidity of chant. In a piece like this, one sees Widor not only forging his own post-Romantic aesthetic and style but also evincing (as in the Praeludium Circulare) a lineage that extends back to the great organ masters of the Renaissance, many of whom also used the Salve Regina as the basis for organ compositions. The sectional character of the movement suggests the *alternatim* practice commonly adopted by the grand organ and choir organ in large French churches. At the end there is a trace of the French classical style when the Pédale Trompette carries the Gregorian melody, accompanied by the Plein Jeu.

The movement exists in two similar versions: *C/C'* and *D/E*. Edition *E* is the principal source.

### Critical Notes

M. 34, staff 2, upper voice, note 2 is g'-natural in all editions—edition follows *Emend* 2. M. 49, staff 2, lower voice, note 2 has eighth flag—an error; edition follows *Emend* 2. M. 74, beat 4–m. 78, staff 2 uses alto clef in both versions.

Version *C/C'* differs from version *D/E* as follows. M. 26, staves 2 and 3 have whole notes tied to eighth notes on m. 27, beat 1. M. 29, crescendo hairpin begins on beat 3 and ends in m. 30 at note 3 of upper voice. M. 30, decrescendo hairpin begins at note 4 of upper voice and ends at note 7; beat 3 has *p*. M. 32, beat 4 has *cresc*. M. 33, beat 2 has no *cresc*. (see report for m. 32) M. 36, staff 2, lower voice is tied d' whole note. M. 41, Pédale coupler is **R**—an error. M. 44, staff 1, lower voice, beat 1 has f' (tied), d' eighth notes; staff 2, beat 3 has f quarter note. M. 47, staff 1, lower voice, beat 3 has g quarter note. M. 48, staves 1 and 3 have no fermatas. M. 49, beat 1, dynamic is *p*; beat 3, staff 1, upper voice has triplet d" (tied), f", g" eighth notes; lower voice has triplet c" (tied) quarter note, b'[-flat] eighth note; staff 2, upper voice has triplet f' quarter note, e' eighth note; lower voice has triplet d' quarter note, c' eighth note; beat 4, staff 1, lower voice has b'[-flat] (tied), d" eighth notes; staff 2, upper voice has e' (tied), d' eighth notes; lower voice has c' (tied), b[-flat] eighth notes. M. 51, staff 2, lower voice, beat 2 has c' (tied) eighth note, d', e' sixteenth notes; beat 3 has d' half note. M. 64, staff 1, upper voice, beats 1–2 have sixteenth rest, g", a", g" eighth notes, e" sixteenth note; beats 3–4 have sixteenth rest, f", g", f" eighth notes, d" sixteenth note. M. 65, staff 1, upper voice, beats 1–4 have sixteenth rest, e", f", e", d", e", f", e", g" eighth notes —an error; the final g" should be sixteenth note. M. 66, staff 1, upper voice, notes 5–6 have no tie.

## V. *Adagio*

The Adagio, of a contemplative and devotional character, exists in four versions: *A/A'*, *B/B'*, *C*, and *C'/D/E*. Version *A/A'* is unique among Widor scores in being written throughout for the Voix humaine; this first version is given in Appendix 5. The three later versions are similar to each other; *C'/D/E* is a bit more developed than *B/B'*, and *C* is a transitional version comprising elements of both. All three later versions incorporate much of the original music, extending it with an introductory Flûte arabesque and with related interludes at the ends of phrases. The later versions also call for a different registrational scheme than the original. For the final version, edition *E* is the principal source.

The curious contradiction between the movement heading, Adagio, and the tempo indication, Andante, finds an explanation in the publication history of the movement's revisions. Editions *A* and *A'* bear only the heading, Adagio. Edition *B* introduces a metronome mark of quarter note equals 50. Edition *C* replaces the metronome mark with Andante, and this is retained in editions *C'*, *D*, and *E*. The inconsistency between movement heading and tempo indication seems never to have captured Widor's attention. If the Adagio of 1872 and the Andante of 1901 were in fact both played at about quarter note equals 50, then the contrary nomenclature provides valuable evidence of a tendency (not untypical of the period) to more deliberate and contemplative performing tempos. Alternatively, it is possible to see the change to Andante as a rejection of the quarter note equals 50 in favor of a brisker tempo. Widor's few recordings, which do favor deliberate (though by no means languid) tempos, likely reflect his aesthetic convictions more than a decline in his technical facility.

### Critical Notes

M. 4, staff 2, upper voice, note 1 is dotted in *C* and *C'/D/E*—an error. M. 32, staff 2, lower voice, note has no dot in *C* and *C'/D/E*—an error. Mm. 47–56, the dynamics directives and hairpins are placed under staff 1—this is likely an error since they can only affect staff 2; or pehaps Widor intended **GR** at m. 46, staff 1, upper voice, and the directive was engraved erroneously.

## VI. *Finale*

The brilliant final movement of the symphony anticipates the popular Toccata from Symphonie V. It exists in five slightly differing versions: *A/A'*, *B/B'/C*, *C'*, *D*, and *E*. Edition *E* is the principal source.

Widor's concern that everything be heard clearly as well as his disapproval of technical display for its own sake led him in edition *E* to revise the tempo indication, Allegro vivace, and metronome mark, half note equals 92, found in all previous editions. The articulation indicated in version *A/A'* is totally staccato; the change to slurred first beats and staccato second, third, and fourth beats occurs in edition *B*. This slur-and-staccato articulation, which gives stress to the strong beats, should be maintained throughout the movement, even when not explicitly marked. In his revisions of articulation Widor customarily marked only the first few measures, assuming that they would serve as a model for the rest of the piece (for the publisher this had the added attraction of saving the expense of reengraving the whole movement). In this Finale, however, Widor went to the trouble of adding many slurs beyond the first few measures, thus removing most ambiguities. The *stacc.* directive in measure 9, meaning "simile" or "sempre staccato," is carried over from version *A/A'* and, of course, must be reinterpreted as applying to everything *except* first beats. Because Widor's intentions are clear, this edition provides articulations only where indicated by the composer. Measures 1–8 are the model to follow, with the possible exception of measures 19–22, where all-staccato articulation may be what is wanted.

Measures 66 and 70 seem to have given Widor some difficulty: one or both of them differ in four of the versions. Likewise, the Pédale part in measures 134–47 differs in three of the versions, and the concluding five measures differ in two of the versions. In all cases the final edition seems to the editor the most refined. The progressive revisions of the last page, especially, clarify the texture and heighten the climactic effect of the last three chords. Versions *A/A'* and *B/B'/C* repeat measures 134–41; this seems to overly prolong the ending, especially with the Pédale droning on D much of the time. The removal of the repeat, revision of the Pédale part, and changes in the last five measures yield the final reading of the last page in edition *C'*.

In all editions subsequent to *A'*, after the initial appearance of manual directives **GPR** (m. 1) and **PR** (m. 31, staff 2), the short forms **G** and **P** are used as a space saver. (The abbreviation of **GPR** to **G** and of **PR** to **P** is not uncommon in the symphonies, and it sometimes causes ambiguity. There should, however, be no doubt that Widor sometimes intended single letters as abbreviations, for he clearly states in his pedagogical writings on organ music that this is his practice when it proves expedient.) In the present edition the short forms are realized editorially as full directives to avoid confusion.

CRITICAL NOTES

M. 17, staff 1, dyads 1–2 are slurred both above and below.   M. 22, staff 1, beat 4, e" is stemmed with g'/a' in *A/A'*.   Mm. 51, 52, and 53, staff 2, beats 1–2, staccato articulations from *A/A'* were never deleted in later editions, although Widor revised the articulation of model mm. 1–8 (see discussion above).   M. 63, the manual directive is only a smudge, if it appears at all, in prints of *E*—edition follows all previous editions; staff 3, note 1, staccato dot faded after edition *B*.   M. 64, staff 3, note 1, staccato dot faded after edition *C'*.

Mm. 117 and 118, staff 3, note 4 is B-sharp in *C'*, *D*, and *E*—an error; the sharps have been inserted in staff 3 instead of directly above in staff 2, middle voice (*A/A'* and *B/B'/C* have no accidentals for note 4 in either staves 2 or 3); edition follows *Emend* 2.   M. 119, staff 2, beat 3 has manual change to Clav. 1 ( = **GPR**) in *A/A'*—the change of manual for the left hand at this point, rather than at m. 121, may be more effective; this could be effected analogously in m. 41 as well.   Mm. 134–47, staff 3, no slurs in any edition—edition follows *Emend* 2.

*Appendix 1*

[I] Prélude. Version *A/A'*. Edition *A'* is the principal source.

*Appendix 2*

I. Prélude. Version *B/B'*, mm. 19–28, 54–100. To perform this version complete, play mm. 1–18 of *A/A'*; then mm. 19–27 from this Appendix; then mm. 28–53 of *A/A'* with changes as given in the critical notes below; then mm. 54–100 from this Appendix. Edition *B'* is the principal source.

M. 83, staff 1, lower voice, beat 2 rest is eighth rest.

Version *B/B'* differs from version *A/A'* in mm. 1–18 as follows. Metronome mark quarter note equals 58 added after Andantino. Registration is "Grand-orgue, Positif, Récit: Fonds de 8—Pédale: Basses de 8 et de 16." M. 1, **GPR** given in lieu of "Clav. 1"; staff 3 has **Péd. GPR.**

Version *B/B'* differs from version *A/A'* in mm. 29–53 as follows.   M. 31, staves 1 and 2, **PR** (with *p* dynamic) given in lieu of "Clav. 2."   Mm. 31, beat 3–m. 35, beat 2, Pédale part moves to staff 2 as lower voice; staff 3 is empty.   M. 35, staves 1 and 2, note 2, *cresc.*   M. 37, staves 1 and 2, crescendo hairpin begins on beat 2 and ends on beat 3.   M. 38, staves 1 and 2, beat 1 has *f* dynamic, beats 2–3 have **GPR** in lieu of "Clav. 1."   M. 41, staff 3 has A (tied), a, A (tied to m. 42) quarter notes.   M. 48 has *poco rit.* on beats 2–3; staves 1 and 2 have decrescendo hairpin that begins on beat 1 and ends on beat 3; staff 2 has lower voice with eighth rest, B-flat eighth note tied to B-flat dotted quarter note, B-flat eighth note; staff 3 has B-flat eighth note (tied), then eighth, quarter, quarter rests.   M. 49 has *a tempo* on beat 3; staves 1 and 2 have crescendo hairpin that begins on beat 1 and ends on beat 3 (beat 3, note 2 has *f* dynamic); staff 2 has lower voice with A-flat dotted half note; staff 3 has quarter, quarter, eighth rests, then A-flat eighth note.

*Appendix 3*

III. Versions *A'/B/B'* and *C/C'*, mm. 1–44. Edition *B'* is the principal source for version *A'/B/B'*; edition *C'* is the principal source for version *C/C'*.

The registration and manual distribution in edition *A'* is slightly different from that in editions *B* and *B'* throughout the movement. The *ossia* in mm. 36–39 is taken from version C/C', which is otherwise like version A'/B/B' throughout. To perform versions A'/B/B' or C/C' complete, play this Appendix, then mm. 38–176 of the final version, D/E (m. 37 in D/E is identical to m. 44 in this Appendix).

M. 6, staff 2, upper voice, notes 1–2 replace a half note in A—this is one of two notational differences between A and A'/B/B'. M. 7, staff 1, natural is incorrectly located above turn symbol in C/C'. M. 49 (= m. 42 in D/E), staff 2, upper voice, notes 1–2 replace f'-sharp half note in A.

Versions A'/B/B' and C/C' differ from version D/E as follows (measure numbers are those in D/E; to obtain the correct measure numbers for versions A'/B/B' and C/C', add 7 to the D/E measure numbers). M. 39, staves 1 and 2 have crescendo hairpin that begins on beat 2 and ends at the barline (not in A'). M. 40, staves 1 and 2 have decrescendo hairpin that begins on beat 1 and ends at beat 3 (not in A'). M. 43, staff 1, upper voice, beats 1 and 2 have a" dotted quarter note, a"-sharp eighth note with turn symbol (natural above) between notes; staves 1 and 2, beats 1–2 have no crescendo hairpin, beat 3 has no *pp* dynamic; staff 2, upper voice, notes 1–2 have no slur. M. 44, registration change is **P** Gambes (no registration change in A')—Récit remains Voix célestes; staff 3, no Pédale couplers indicated. M. 45, staff 1, upper voice, notes 1 and 2 are eighth notes; staff 2, upper voice enters on beat 2 with d half note. M. 47, staff 2, upper voice enters on beat 2 with d half note. M. 59, staff 3, note 2 is B-natural in A'/B/B'. M. 82, staff 3, note 2 is B-sharp (see also the discussion of m. 82 in critical notes to D/E).

## Appendix 4

IV. *Scherzo*. Version A/A'/B/B'. Replaced in edition C by the Salve Regina, this Scherzo is the original fourth movement to the symphony. During its opening four-voice fugal exposition, in a bright six-eight meter, the piece looks like it is going to be Widor's "Gigue Fugue"; but fugal technique is abandoned and instead a frolicsome scherzo unfolds, played staccato throughout. There is only one version of this piece, though a small change in the registration was made at the time of edition B: the Pédale registration in version A/A' is "Anches de 16 et 8." In these symphonies Widor sometimes uses the **G** directive in lieu of **GPR** to save space in an already crowded score (see commentary for VI. Finale). In this movement the opening manual registration "**GPR** anches de 4 et 8" indicates that all three manuals are to be coupled, even though only **G** and **R** directives are used throughout. This edition gives **GPR.** Manual to Pédale couplers are left to the organist's discretion. At all times the player must decide what achieves a balanced result.

It is the editor's opinion that this Scherzo is better suited to the overall character of the symphony than is the Salve Regina, and it may well be reinstated in place of the latter movement for performances of the complete symphony. See the discussion on page xvii of the Preface to this series. Edition B' is the principal source.

M. 126, staff 1, note 1 is also stemmed up as quarter note. M. 141, staff 1, beat 1, editorial staccato follows editions A and A'—the dot evidently faded as early as edition B.

## Appendix 5

[V] *Adagio*. Version A/A'. Critical notes sufficient to make easy the reconstruction of the first version would be very cumbersome and unwieldy. And since the original is so well conceived for the Voix humaine alone, it merits reprinting in its own right. It is the editor's opinion that the symphony would lose nothing were the performer to choose this version in a performance of the whole. Even though most of its music was incorporated into the later versions, their numerous variants blur the unalloyed directness of the original. Edition A' is the principal source.

John R. Near

# Widor's *Avant-propos*

Although it may not be customary to place a preface at the front of musical editions, I believe it is necessary to put one here in order to explain the character, the style, the procedures of registration, and the sign conventions of these eight symphonies.

Old instruments had almost no reed stops: two colors, white and black, foundation stops and mixture stops—that was their entire palette; moreover, each transition between this white and this black was abrupt and rough; the means of graduating the body of sound did not exist. Consequently, Bach and his contemporaries deemed it pointless to indicate registrations for their works—the mixture stops traditionally remaining appropriate to rapid movements, and the foundation stops to pieces of a more solemn pace.

The invention of the "swell box" dates back to just before the end of the eighteenth century. In a work published in 1772, the Dutchman Hess de Gouda expresses the admiration he felt upon hearing Handel, in London, coming to grips with the new device; some time later, in 1780, Abbé Vogler recommends the use of the "box" in the German manufacture of instruments. The idea gained ground, but without great artistic effect—for in spite of the most perspicacious efforts, they did not succeed in going beyond the limits of a thirty-key manual and an insignificant number of registers.

It was necessary to wait until 1839 for the solution to the problem.

The honor for it redounds to French industry and the glory to Mr. A. Cavaillé-Coll. It is he who conceived the diverse wind pressures, the divided windchests, the pedal systems and the combination registers, he who applied for the first time Barker's pneumatic motors, created the family of harmonic stops, reformed and perfected the mechanics to such a point that each pipe—low or high, loud or soft—instantly obeys the touch of the finger, the keys becoming as light as those of a piano—the resistances being suppressed, rendering the combination of [all] the forces of the instrument practical. From this result: the possibility of confining an entire division in a sonorous prison—opened or closed at will—the freedom of mixing timbres, the means of intensifying them or gradually tempering them, the freedom of tempos, the sureness of attacks, the balance of contrasts, and, finally, a whole blossoming of wonderful colors—a rich palette of the most diverse shades: harmonic flutes, gambas, bassoons, English horns, trumpets, celestes, flue stops and reed stops of a quality and variety unknown before.

The modern organ is essentially symphonic. The new instrument requires a new language, an ideal other than scholastic polyphony. It is no longer the Bach of the fugue whom we invoke but the heartrending melodist, the preeminently expressive master of the Preludes, the Magnificat, the B-minor Mass, the cantatas, and the *St. Matthew Passion*.

But this "expressiveness" of the new instrument can only be subjective; it arises from mechanical means and cannot have spontaneity. While the stringed and wind instruments of the orchestra, the piano, and voices reign only by naturalness of accent and unexpectedness of attack, the organ, clothed in its primordial majesty, speaks as a philosopher: alone among all, it can put forth the same volume of sound indefinitely and thus inspire the religious idea of the infinite. Surprises and accents are not natural to it; they are lent to it, they are accents by adoption. It is clear that their use requires tact and discernment. It is also clear to what extent the organ symphony differs from the orchestral symphony. No confusion is to be feared. One will never write indiscriminately for the orchestra or for the organ, but henceforth one will have to exercise the same care with the combination of timbres in an organ composition as in an orchestral work.

Rhythm itself must come under the influence of modern trends: it must lend itself to a sort of elasticity of the measure, all the while preserving its rights. It must allow the musical phrase to punctuate its paragraphs and breathe when necessary, provided that it hold [the phrase] by the bit and that [the phrase] march to its step. Without rhythm, without this constant manifestation of the will returning periodically to the strong beat, the performer will not be listened to. How often the composer hesitates and abstains at the moment of writing on his score the *poco ritenuto* that he has in his thought! He does not dare, from fear that the exaggeration of the performer may weaken or break the flow of the piece. The indication is left out. We do not have the graphic means for emphasizing the end of a period, or reinforcing a chord by a type of pause of unnoticeable duration. Isn't it a great shame, especially since the organ is an instrument that draws all of its effect from time values?

As to terminology, the system indicating the disposition of timbres—usage having established nothing as yet—it seemed practical to me to note the manual and pedal registration at the head of each piece; to apportion by tone colors, rather than an exact nomenclature of stops, the intensity of the sonorities of the same family; to designate the manuals by their abbreviations (two or more initials juxtaposed signifying the coupling of two or more manuals); to assume the reed stops always prepared; and finally to reserve *fff* for the full power of the organ, without having to mention the introduction of the ventil (Anches) pedals. In the combination **GR**

[Grand-orgue, Récit], the crescendo applies only to the Récit, unless this crescendo leads to the *fff*, in which case all the forces of the instrument must enter little by little in order, flues and reeds.

It is unnecessary, I believe, to implore the same precision, the same coordination of the feet and hands in leaving a keyboard as in attacking it, and to protest against all carrying-over of the pedal after the time, an old-fashioned custom that has happily almost disappeared.

With the consummate musicians of today, the insufficiencies and shortcomings in musical notation become less worrisome; the composer is more certain of seeing his intentions understood and his implications perceived. Between him and the performer is a steadfast collaboration, which the growing number of virtuosos will render more intimate and fruitful every day.

Ch. M. W.

Symphonie II in D Major

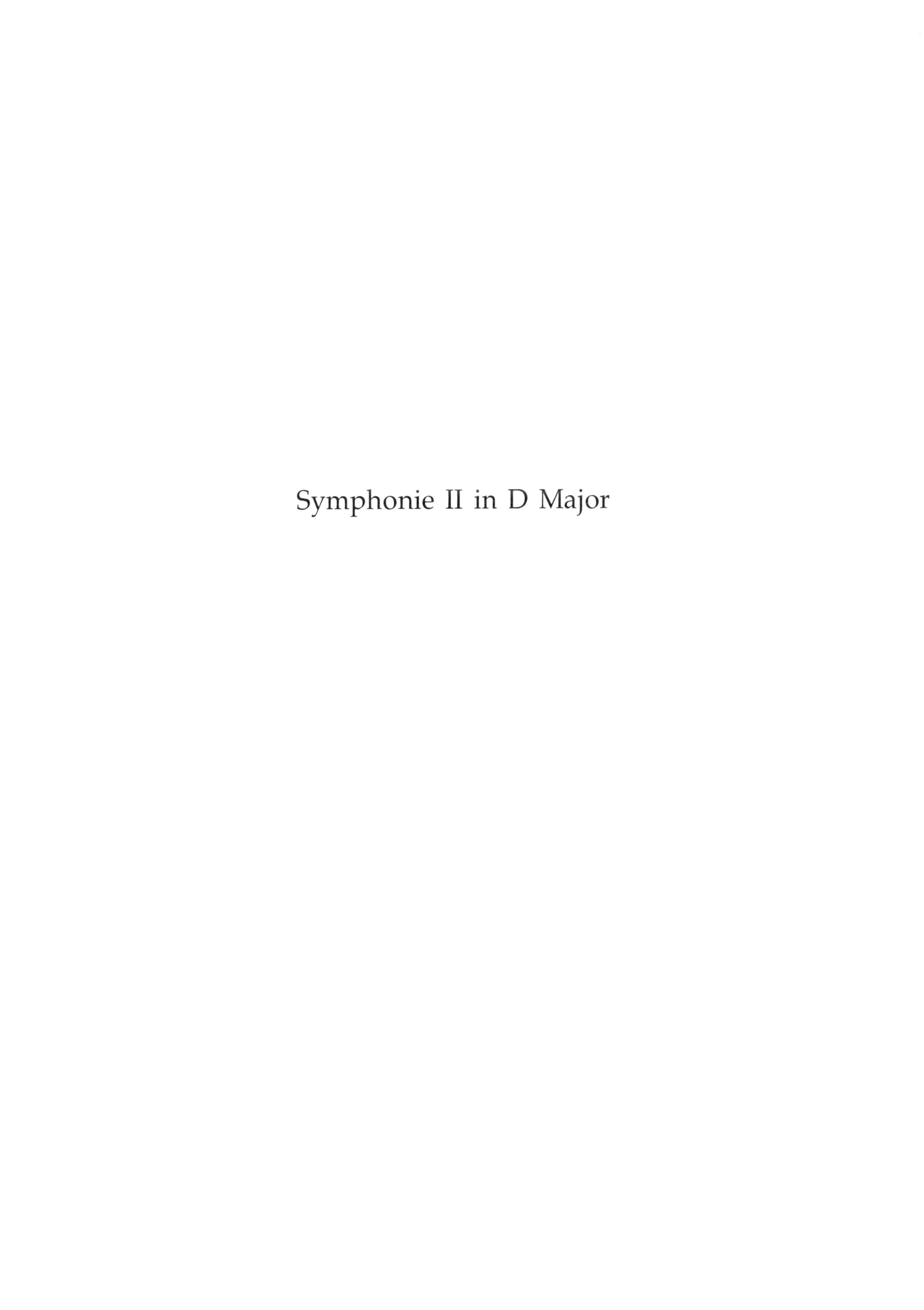

Grand orgue: Fonds 8'
Positif: Fonds 8'
Récit: Fonds 8'
Pédale: Basses 16', 8'

# I. Praeludium Circulare

**Andantino** ($\quarternote = 58$)

GPR $f$

Péd. GPR

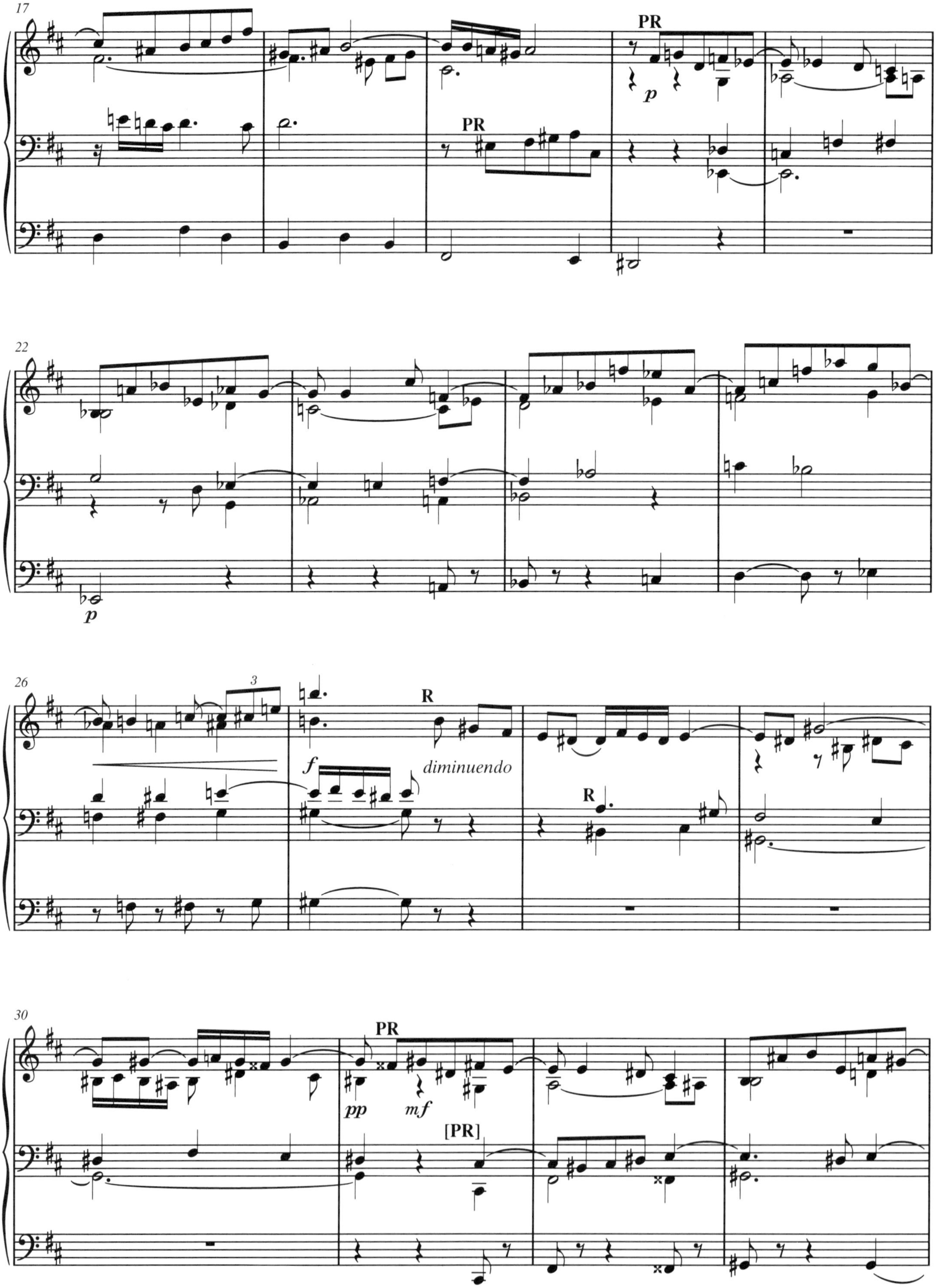
17
PR
p
PR
22
p
26
3
R
f
diminuendo
R
30
PR
pp
mf
[PR]

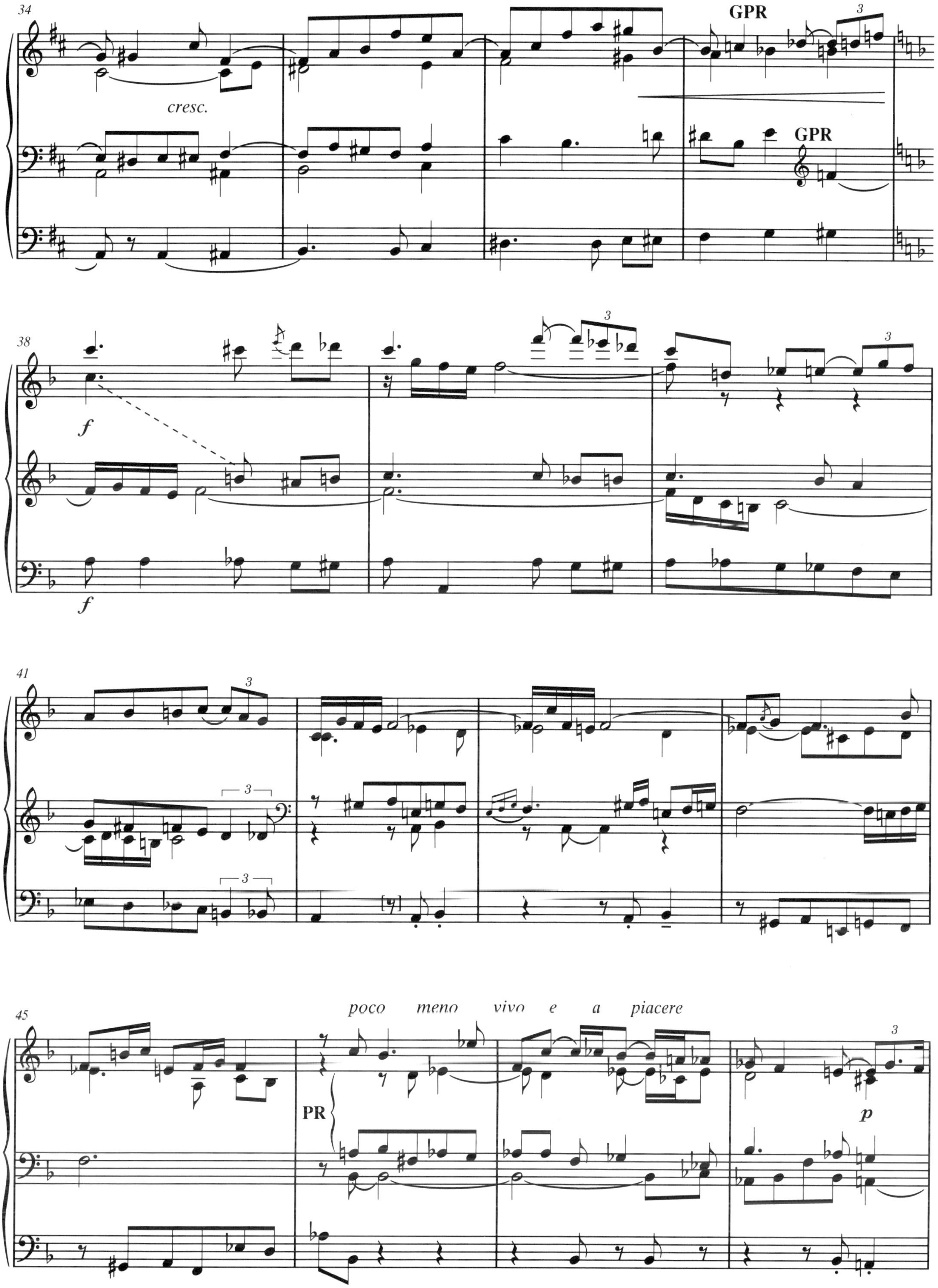
34
cresc.
GPR
GPR
38
f
f
41
45
poco meno vivo e a piacere
PR
p

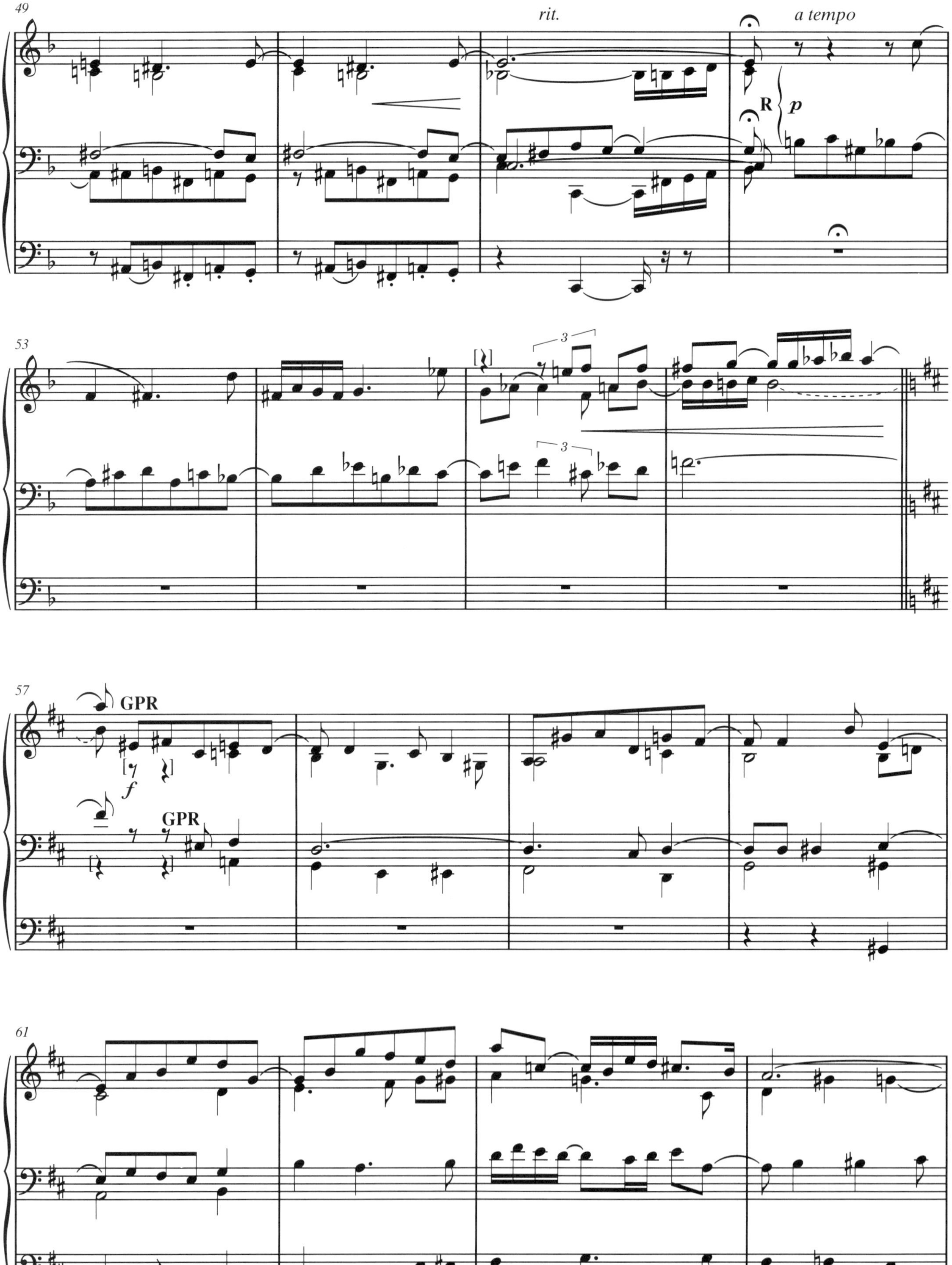
49
rit.
a tempo
R
p
53
3
57
GPR
f
61

65
a piacere
a tempo
69
PR
R
72
rit.
Moderato
R Flûtes 8', 4'
R
p
75
rit.
3
f
GR
GR

Grand orgue: Fonds 16', 8', 4'
Positif: Flûte 8'
Récit: Hautbois 8'
Pédale: Flûte 8'

# II. Pastorale

**Moderato** (♩. = 88)

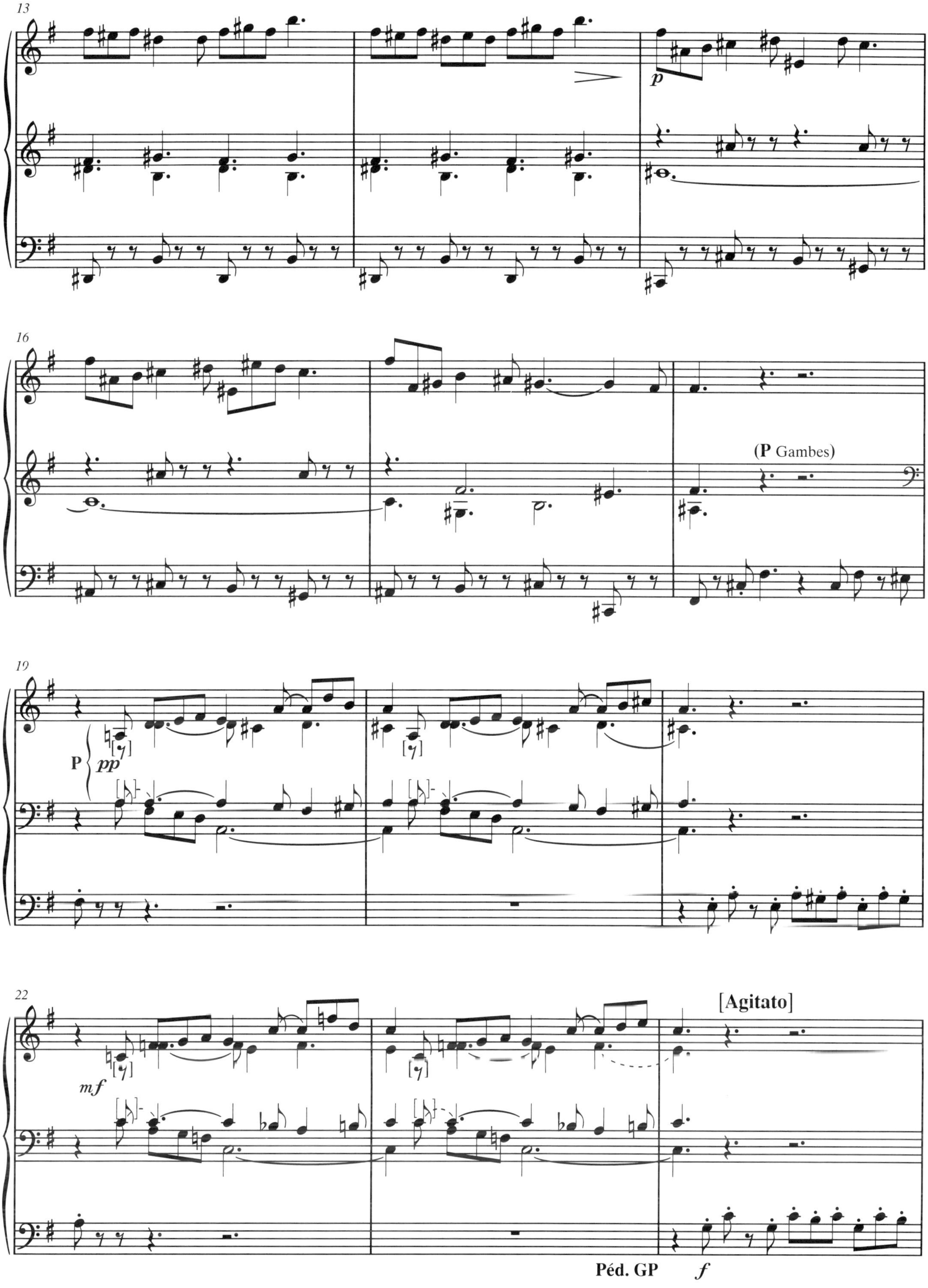
13
16
(P Gambes)
19
P
pp
22
mf
[Agitato]
Péd. GP
f

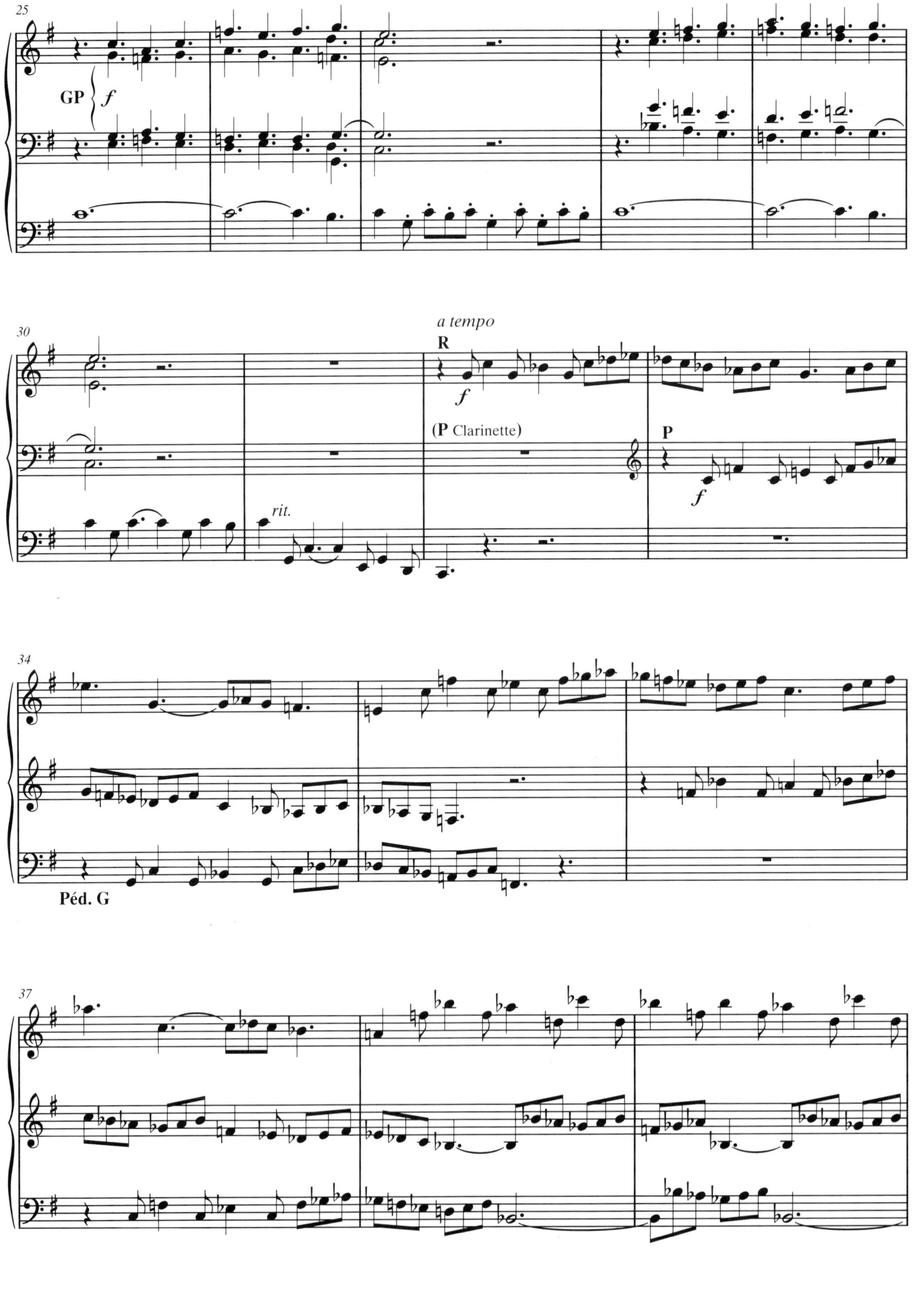
25
GP
f
30
a tempo
R
f
(P Clarinette)
P
f
rit.
34
Péd. G
37

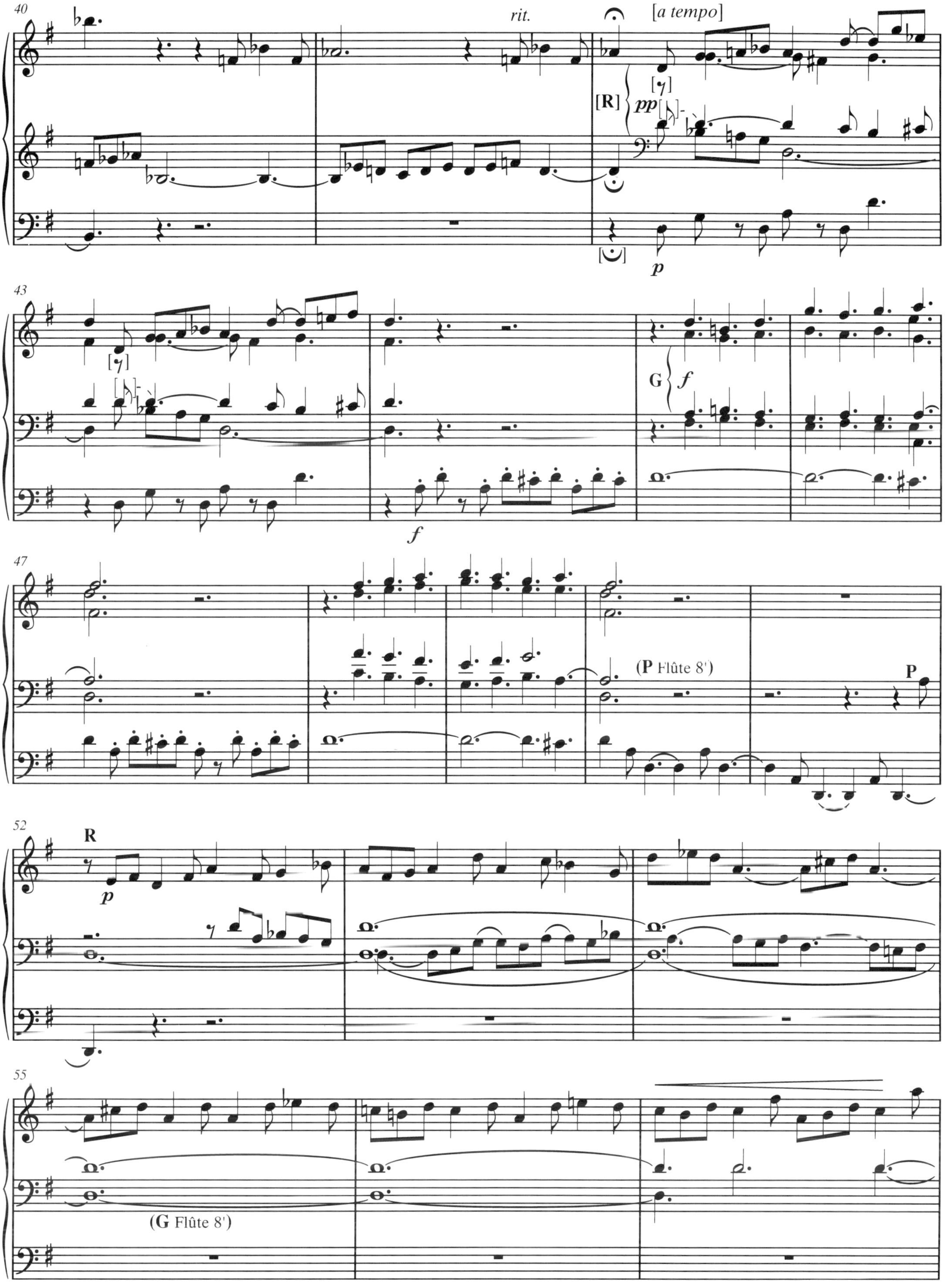
40
rit.
[a tempo]
[R]
pp
p
43
G
f
f
47
(P Flûte 8')
P
52
R
p
55
(G Flûte 8')

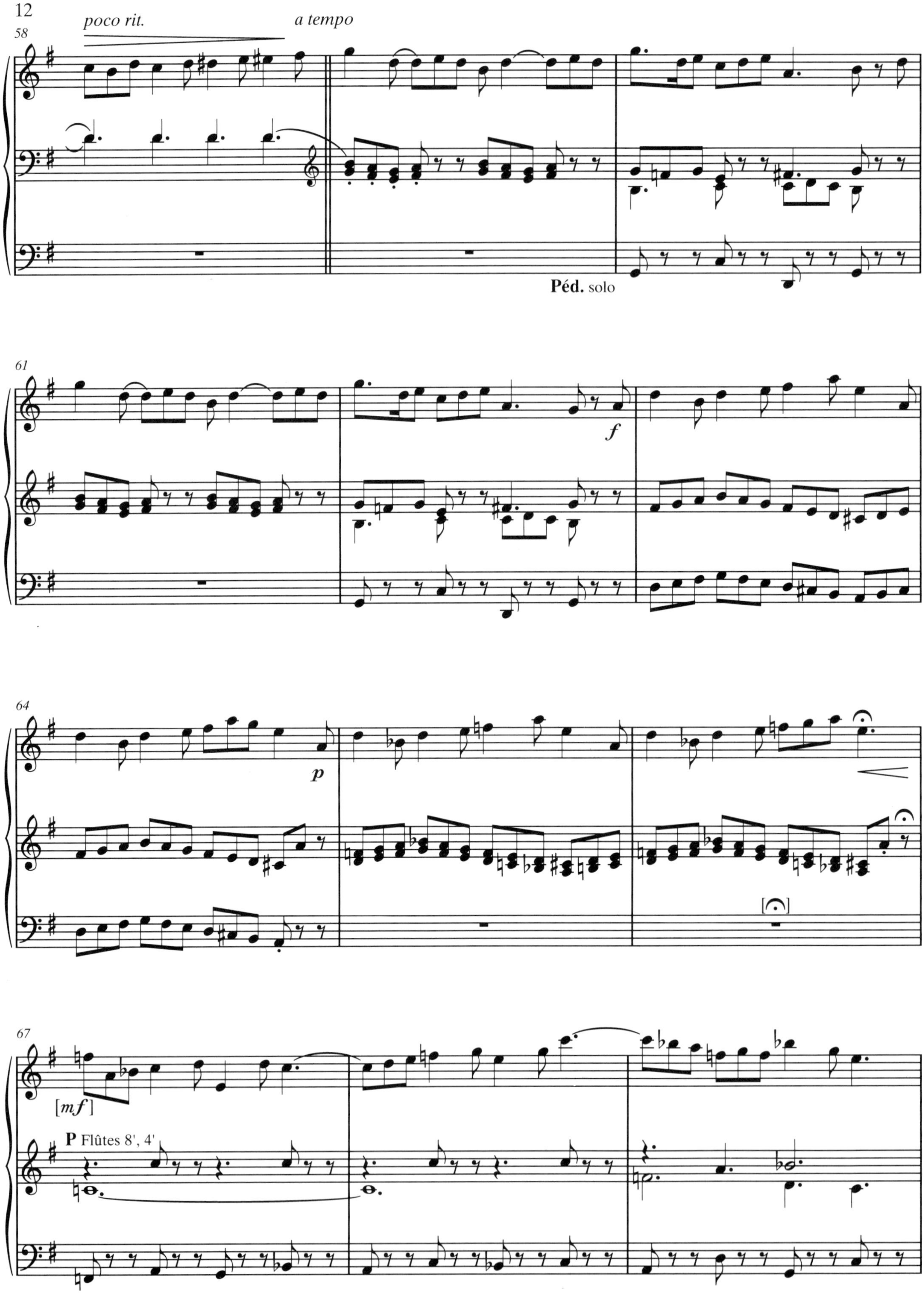
poco rit.
a tempo
58
Péd. solo
61
f
64
p
[𝄐]
67
[mf]
P Flûtes 8', 4'

13

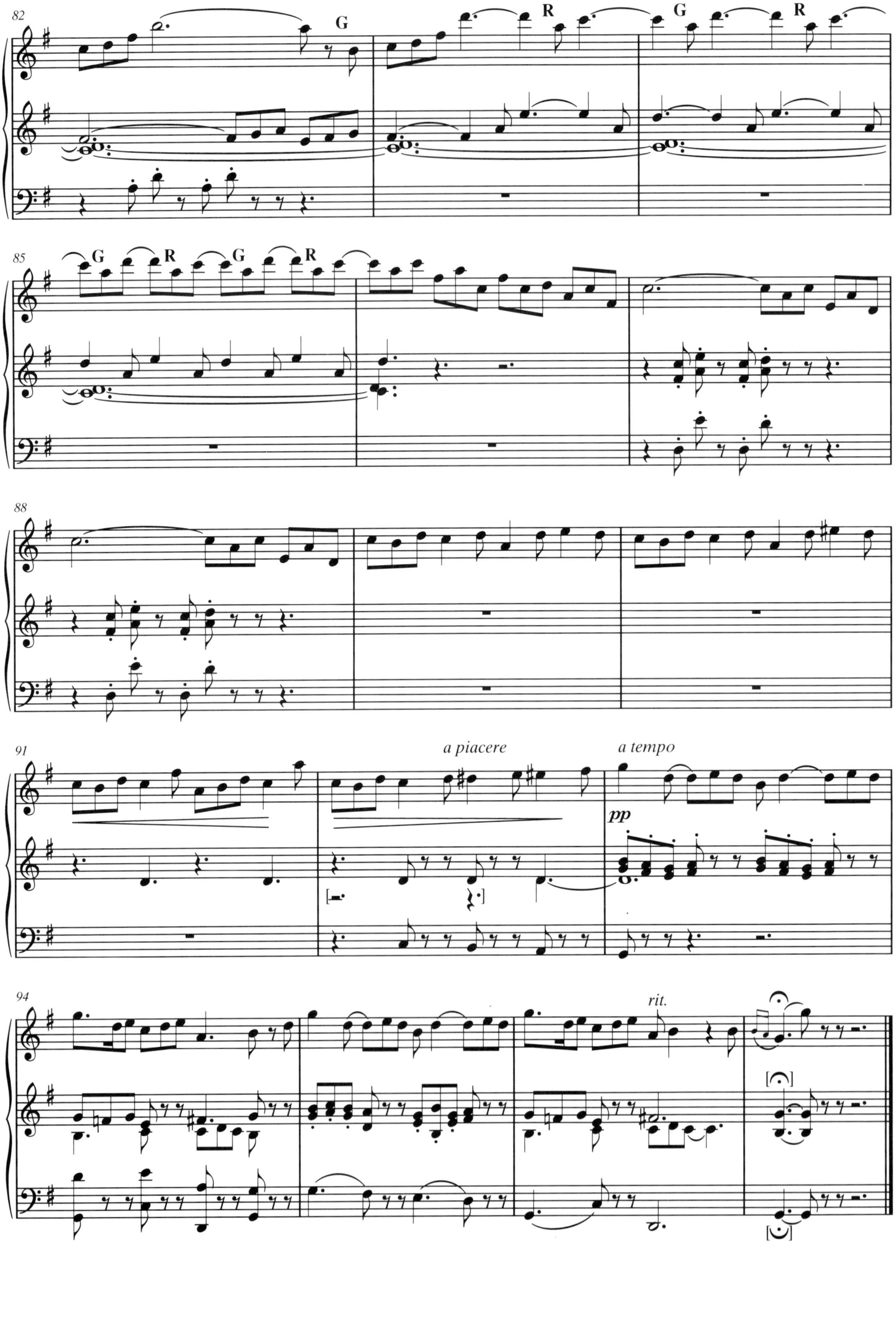
82
G
R
85
88
91
a piacere
a tempo
pp
94
rit.

Grand orgue: Fonds 8'
Positif: Flûte 8'
Récit: Flûtes 8', 4'
Pédale: Fonds 16', 8'

# III

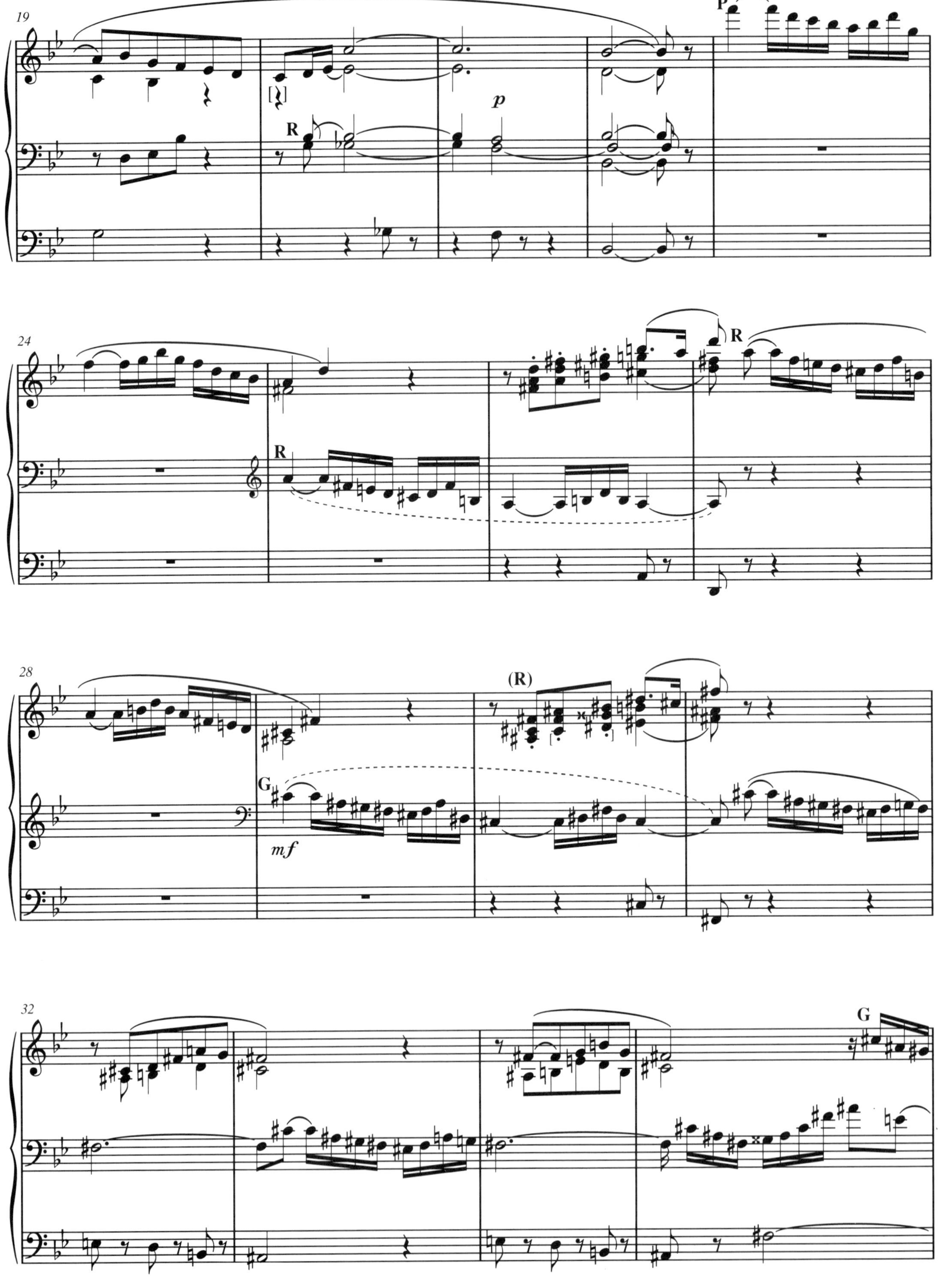
19
P
R
p
24
R
R
28
(R)
G
mf
32
G

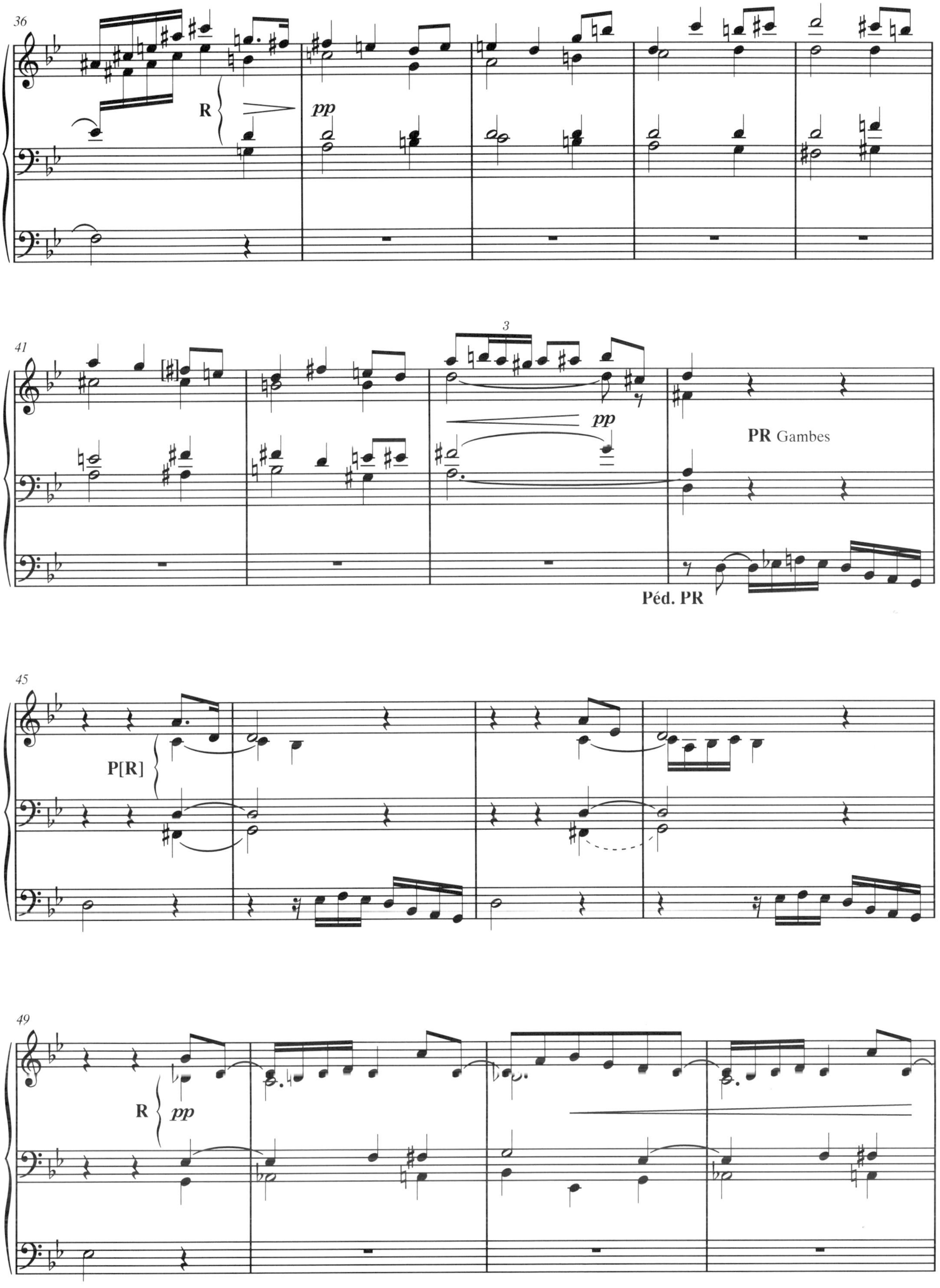
36
R
pp
41
3
pp
PR Gambes
Péd. PR
45
P[R]
49
R
pp

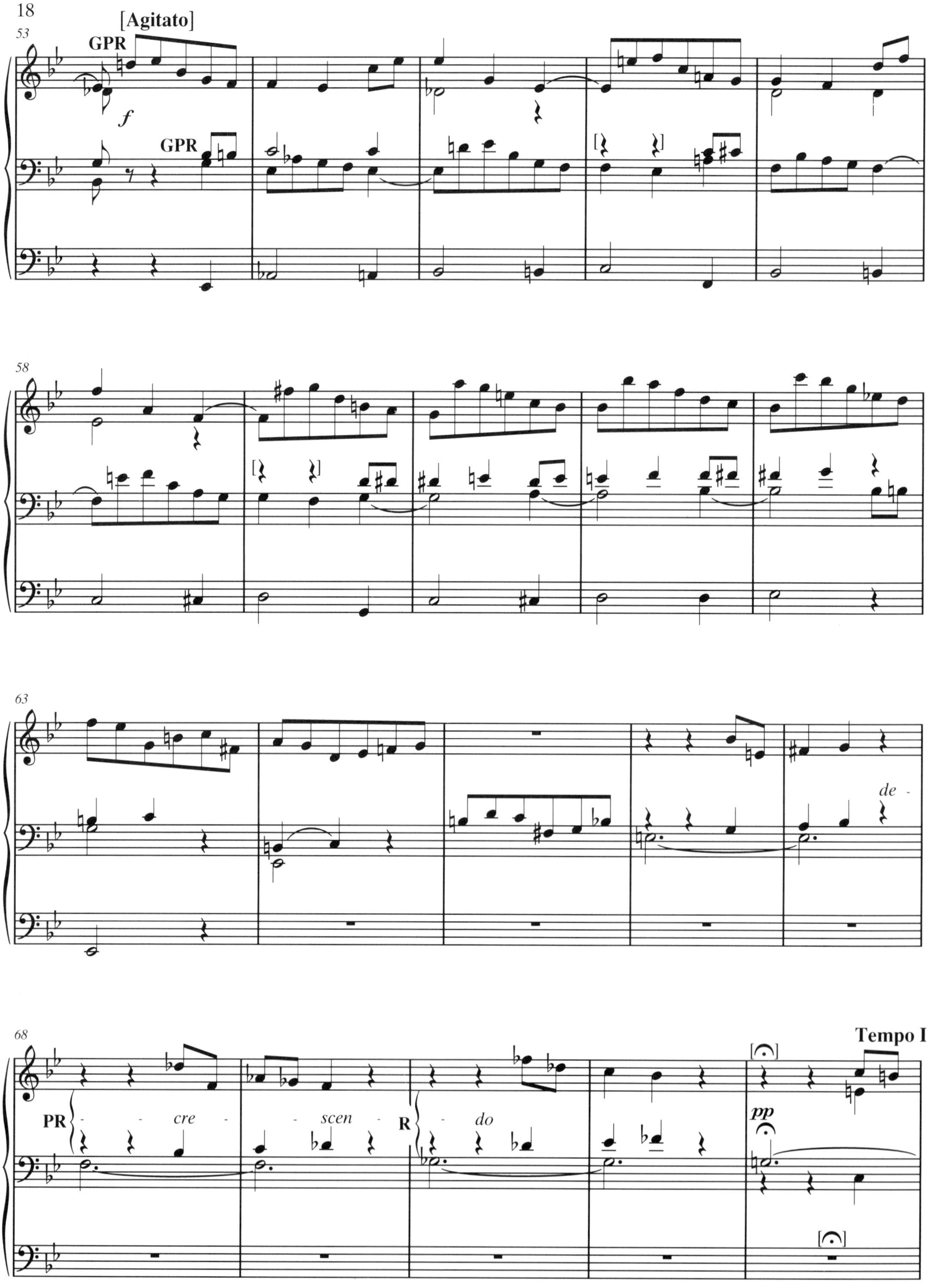
[Agitato]
GPR
f
GPR
de -
PR
cre
scen
R
do
pp
Tempo I

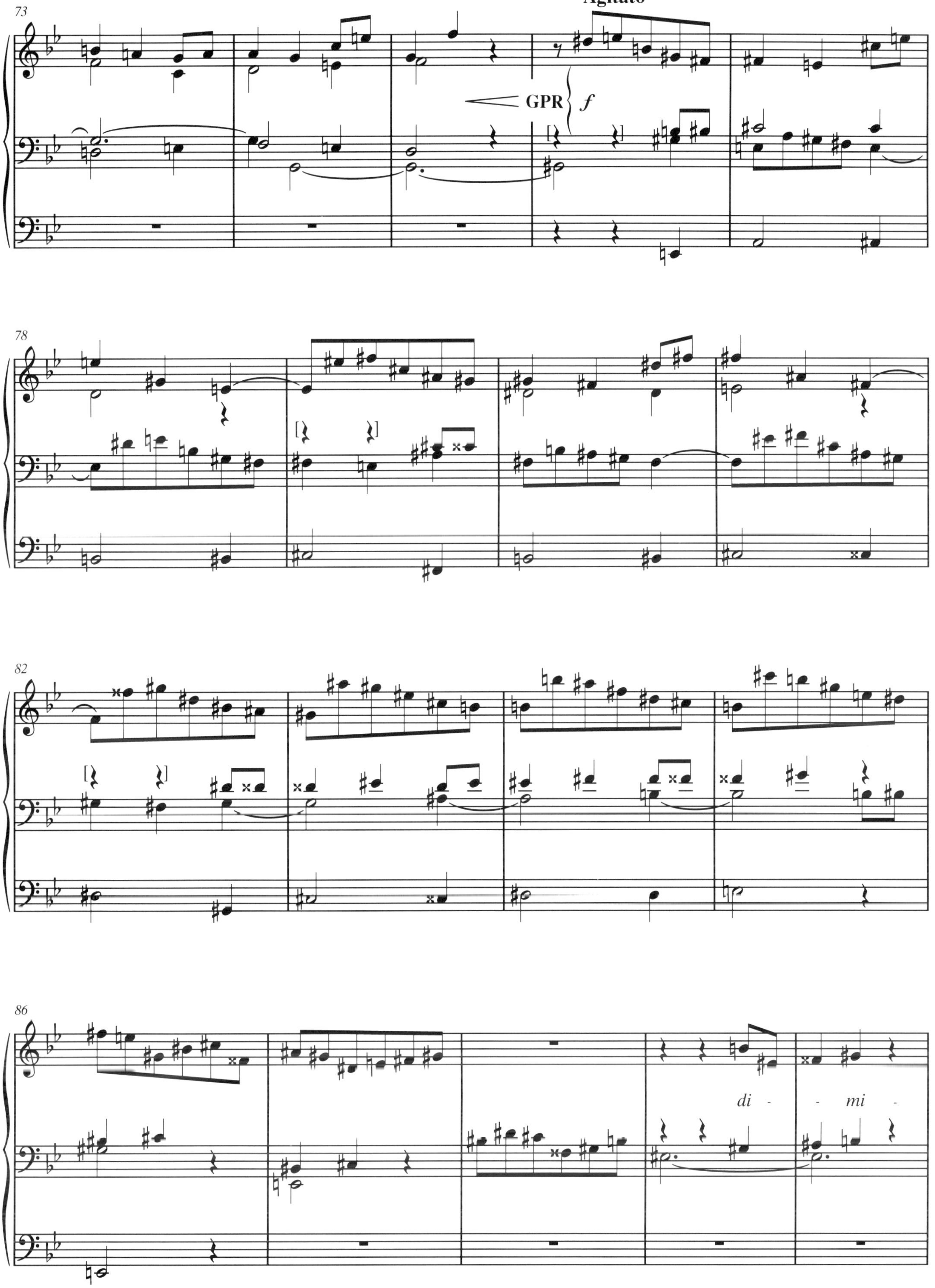
73
Agitato
GPR
f
78
82
86
di - - mi -

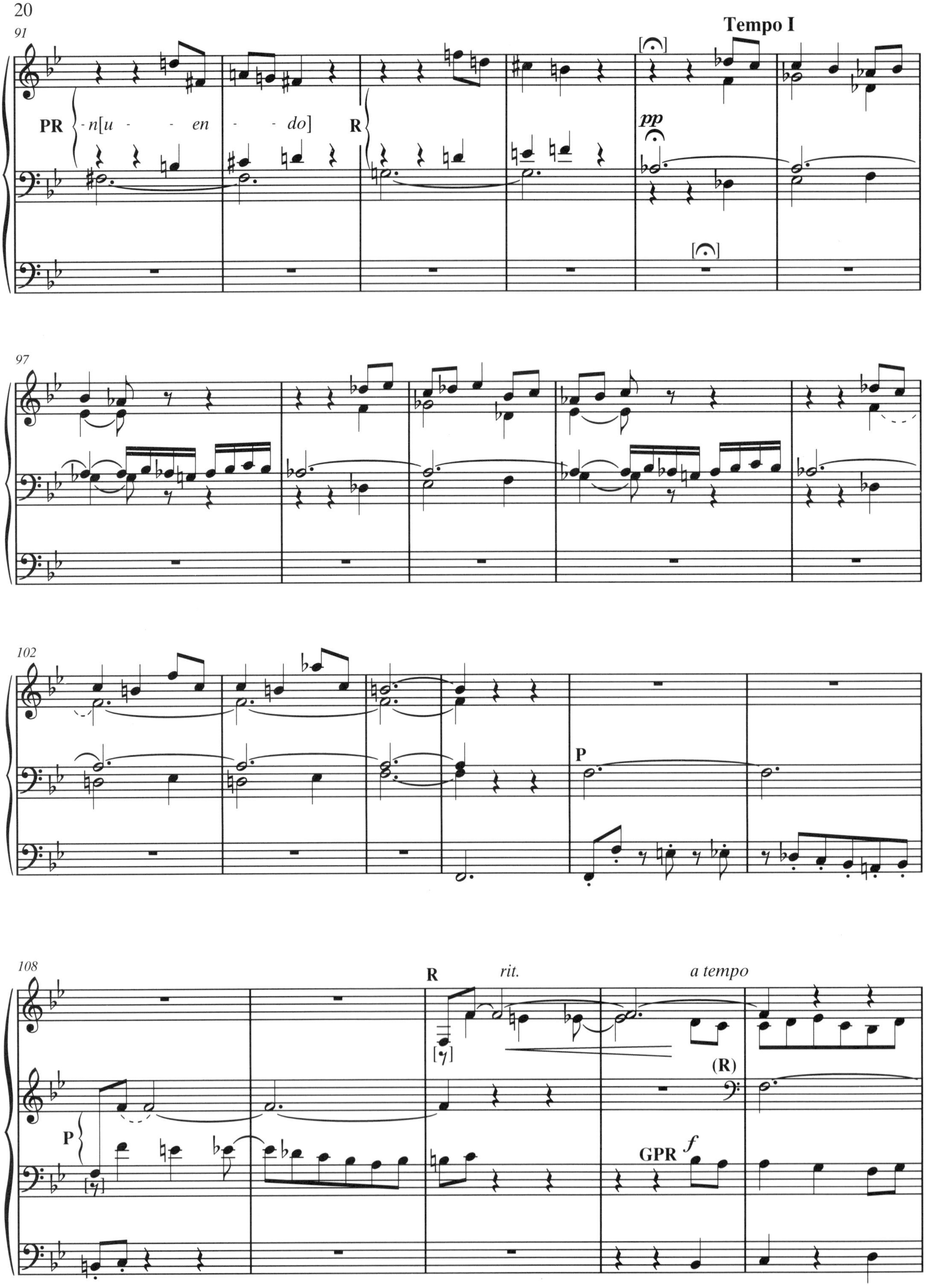
91
Tempo I
PR
-n[u - - en - - do]
R
pp
97
102
P
108
R
rit.
a tempo
(R)
P
GPR
f

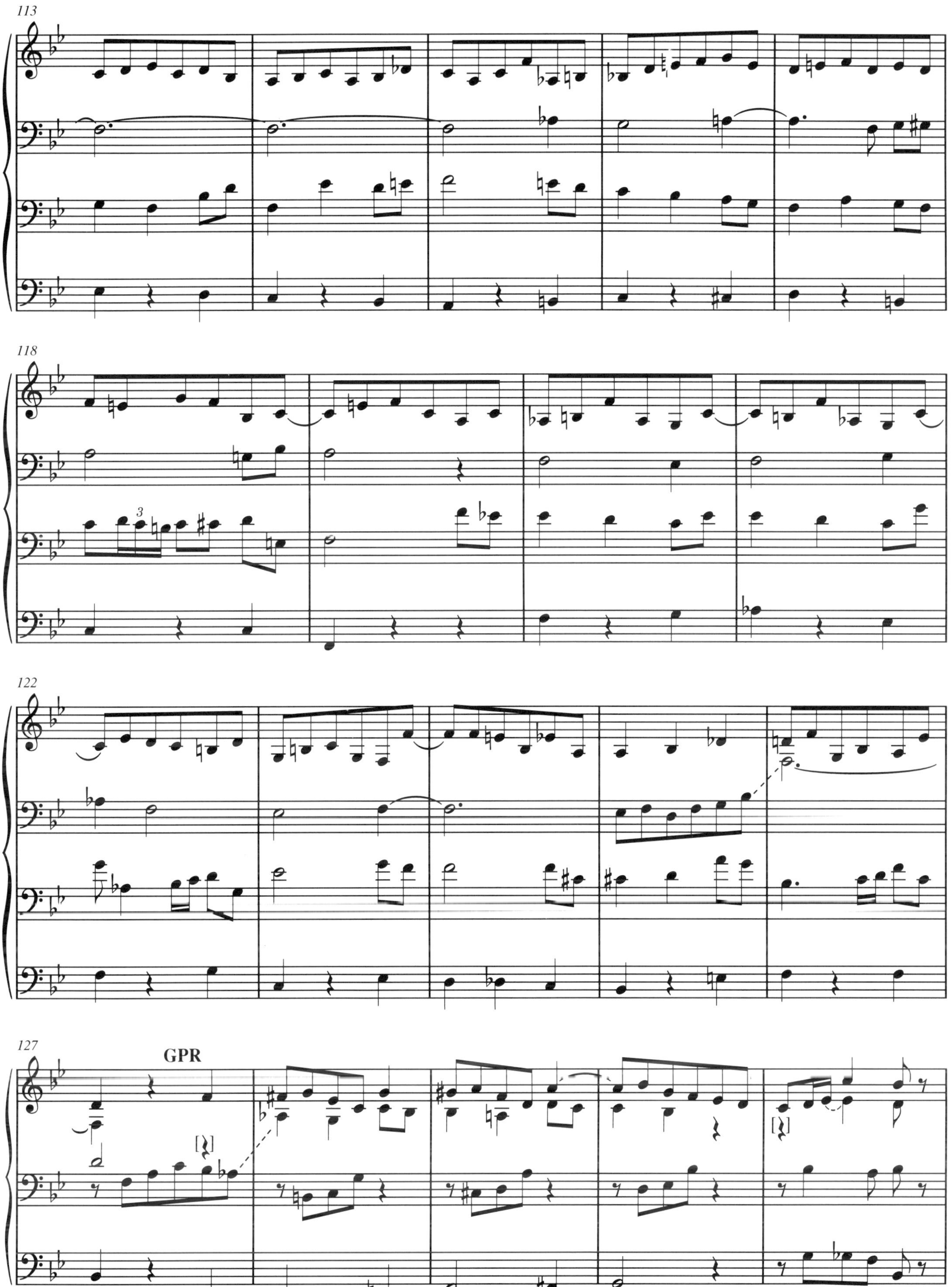
113
118
3
122
127
GPR

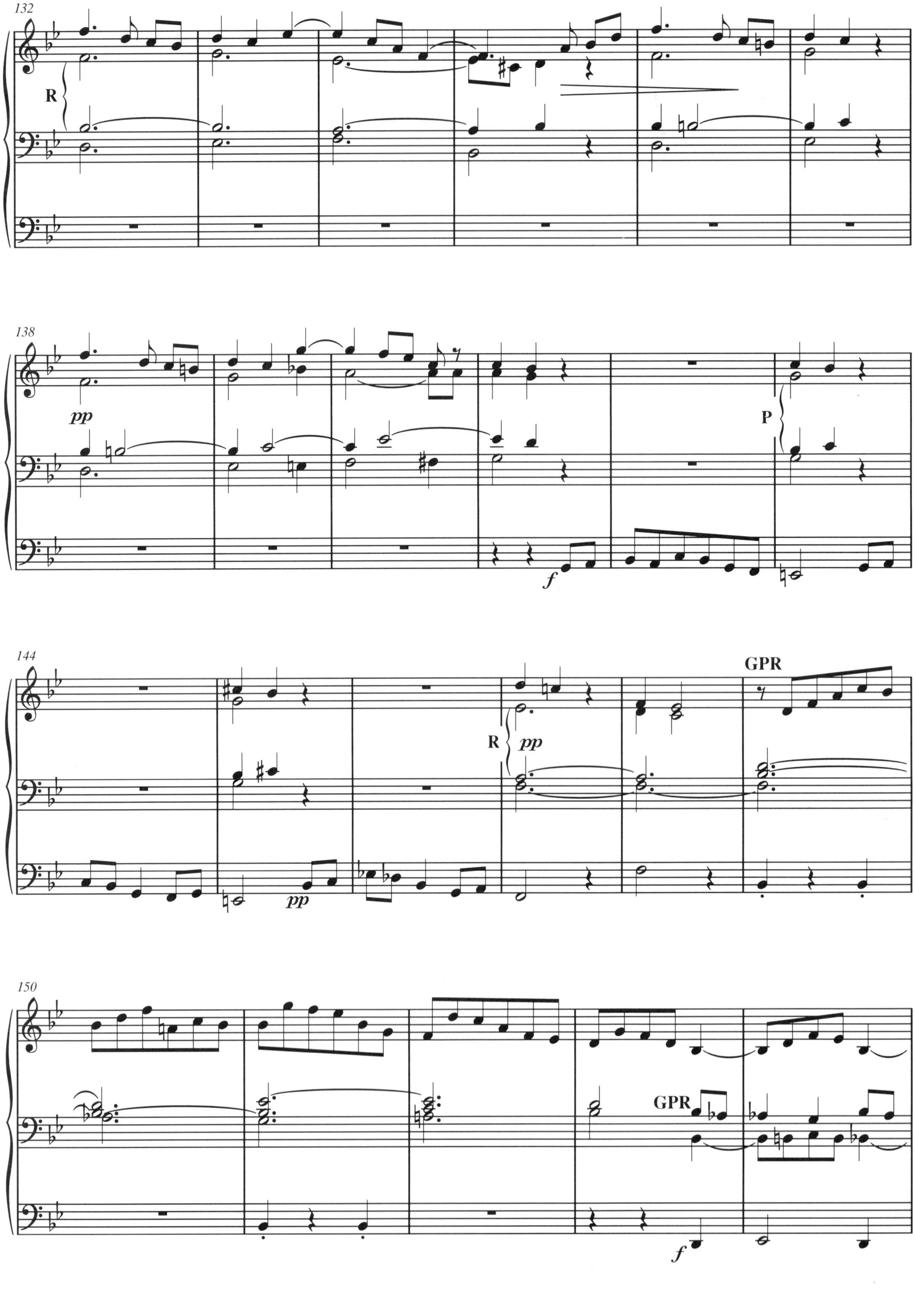
132
R
138
pp
P
f
144
GPR
R
pp
pp
150
GPR
f

23

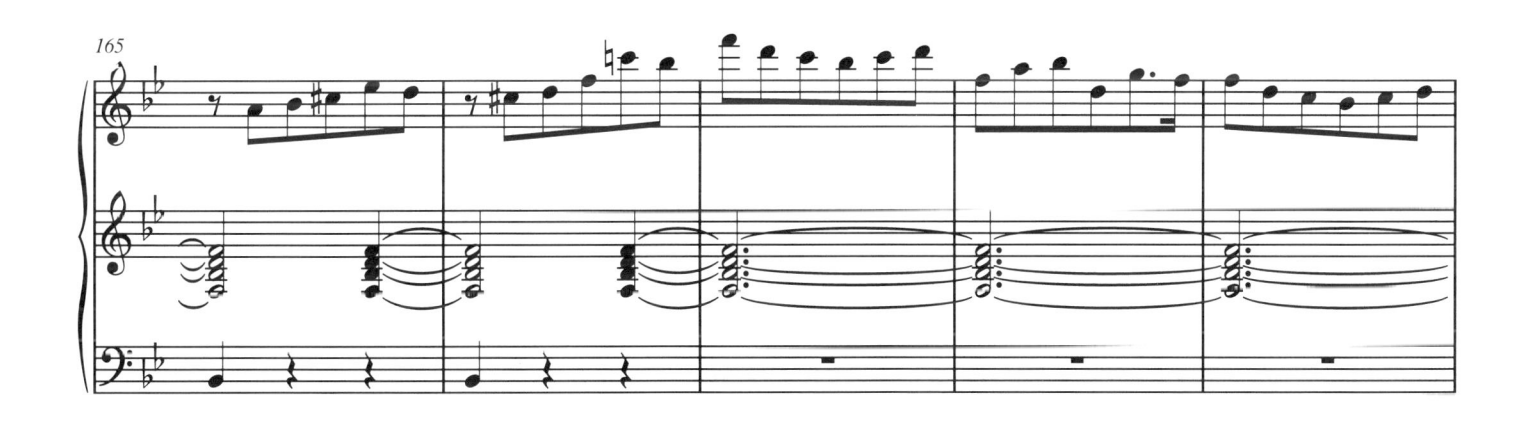

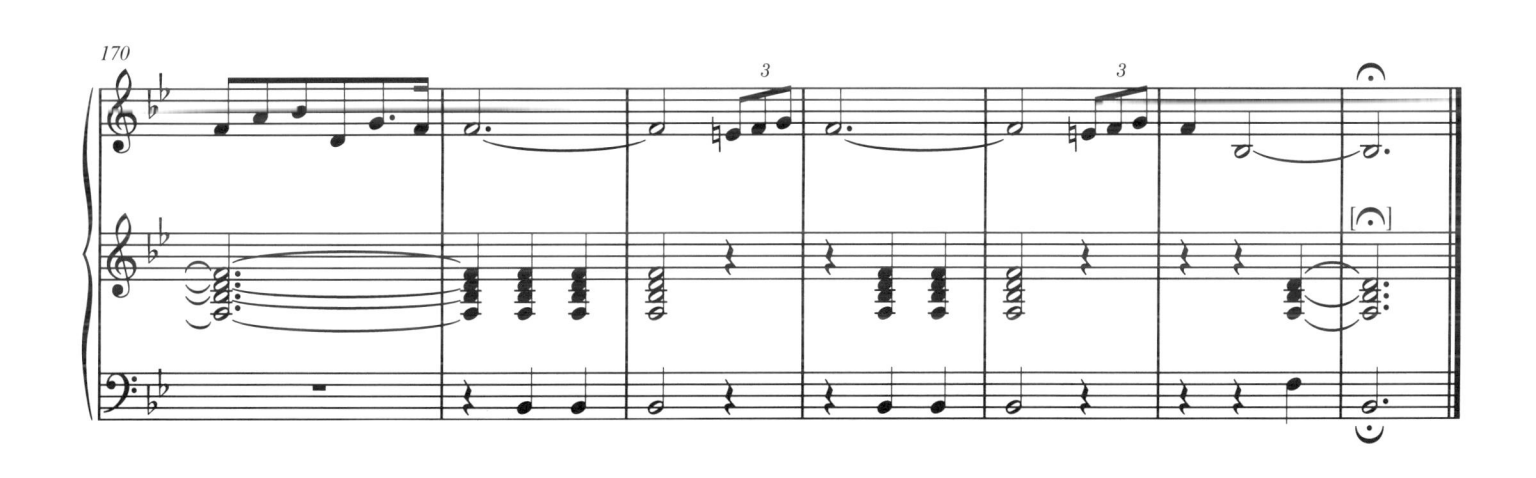

Grand orgue: Fonds 8'
Positif: Flûtes 8', 4'
Récit: [Fonds 8', 4'], Mixtures
Pédale: Flûte 8'

# IV. Salve Regina

**Tranquillamente assai**

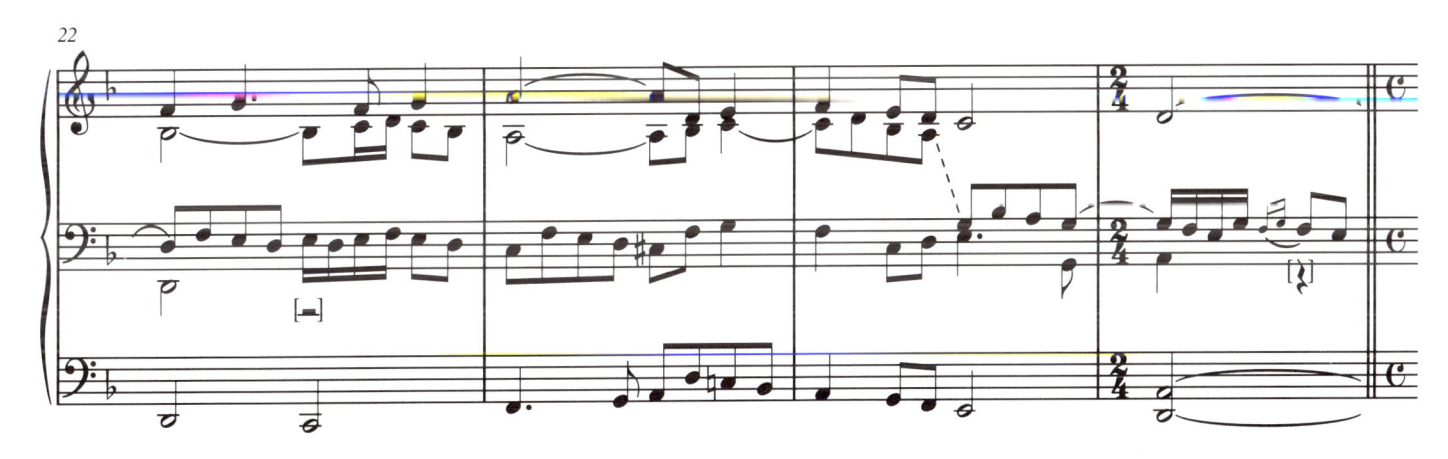

Péd. G

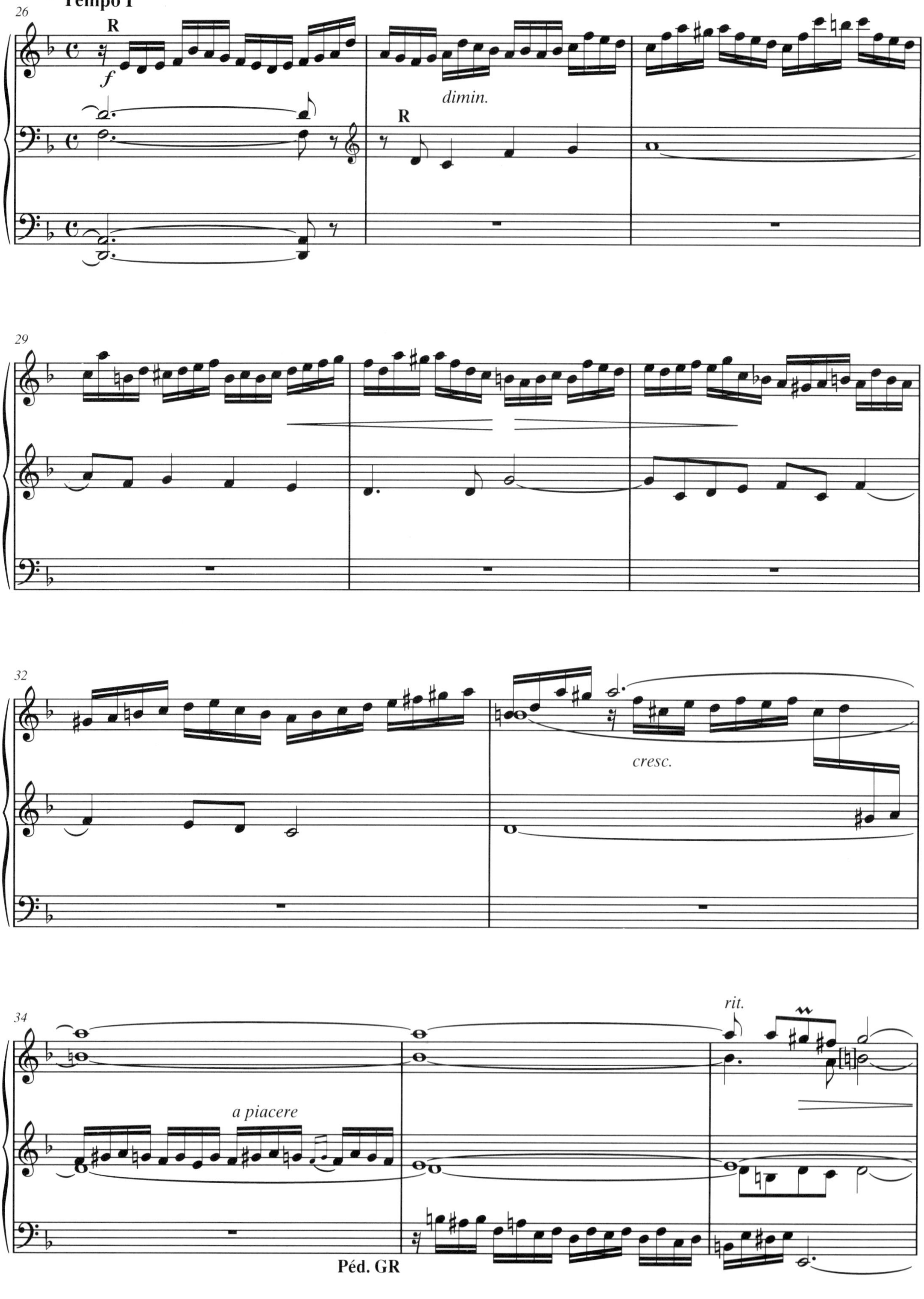
Tempo I
26
R
f
dimin.
R
29
32
cresc.
34
a piacere
rit.
Péd. GR

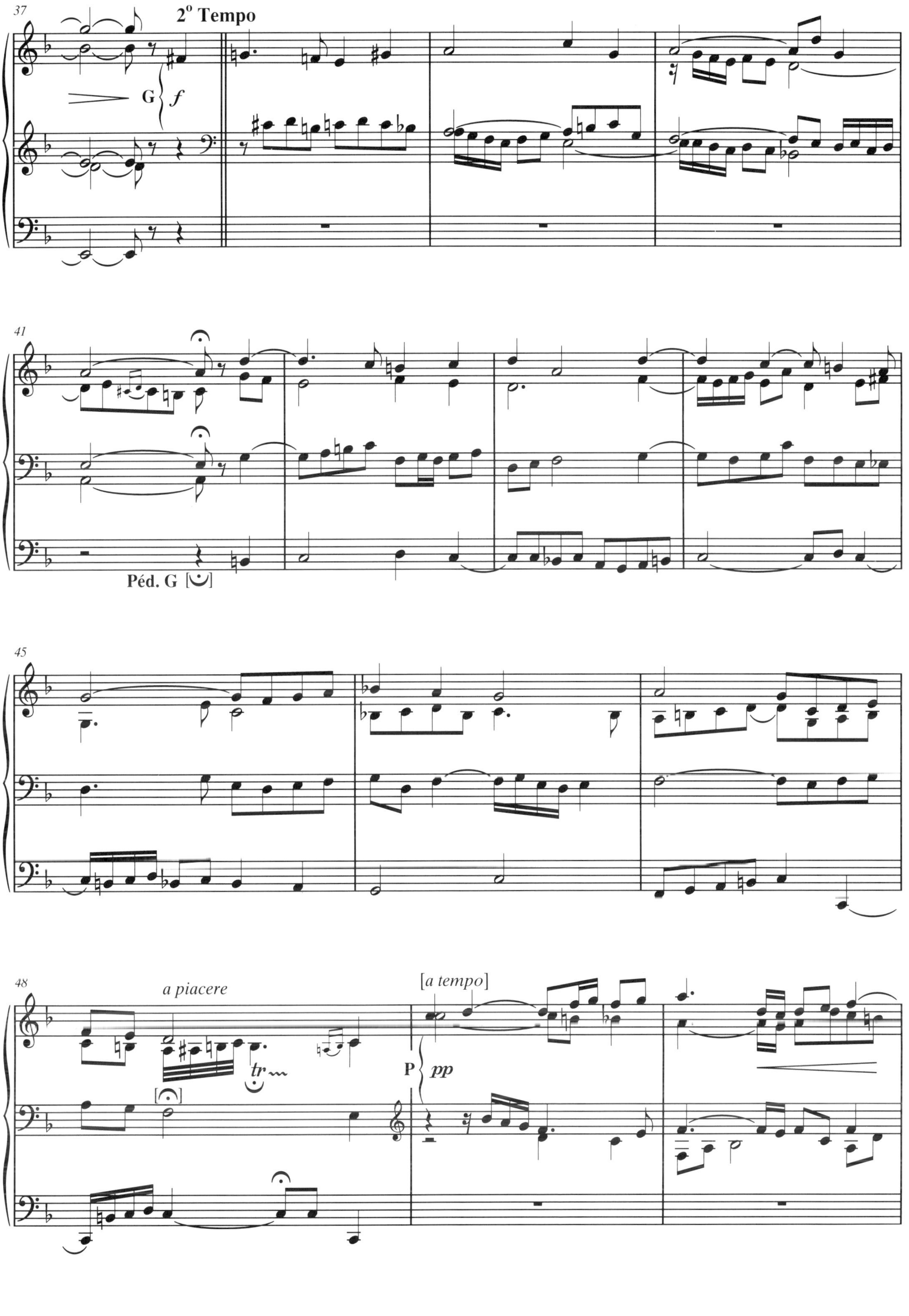
37
2º Tempo
G
f
41
Péd. G
45
48
a piacere
tr
[a tempo]
P
pp

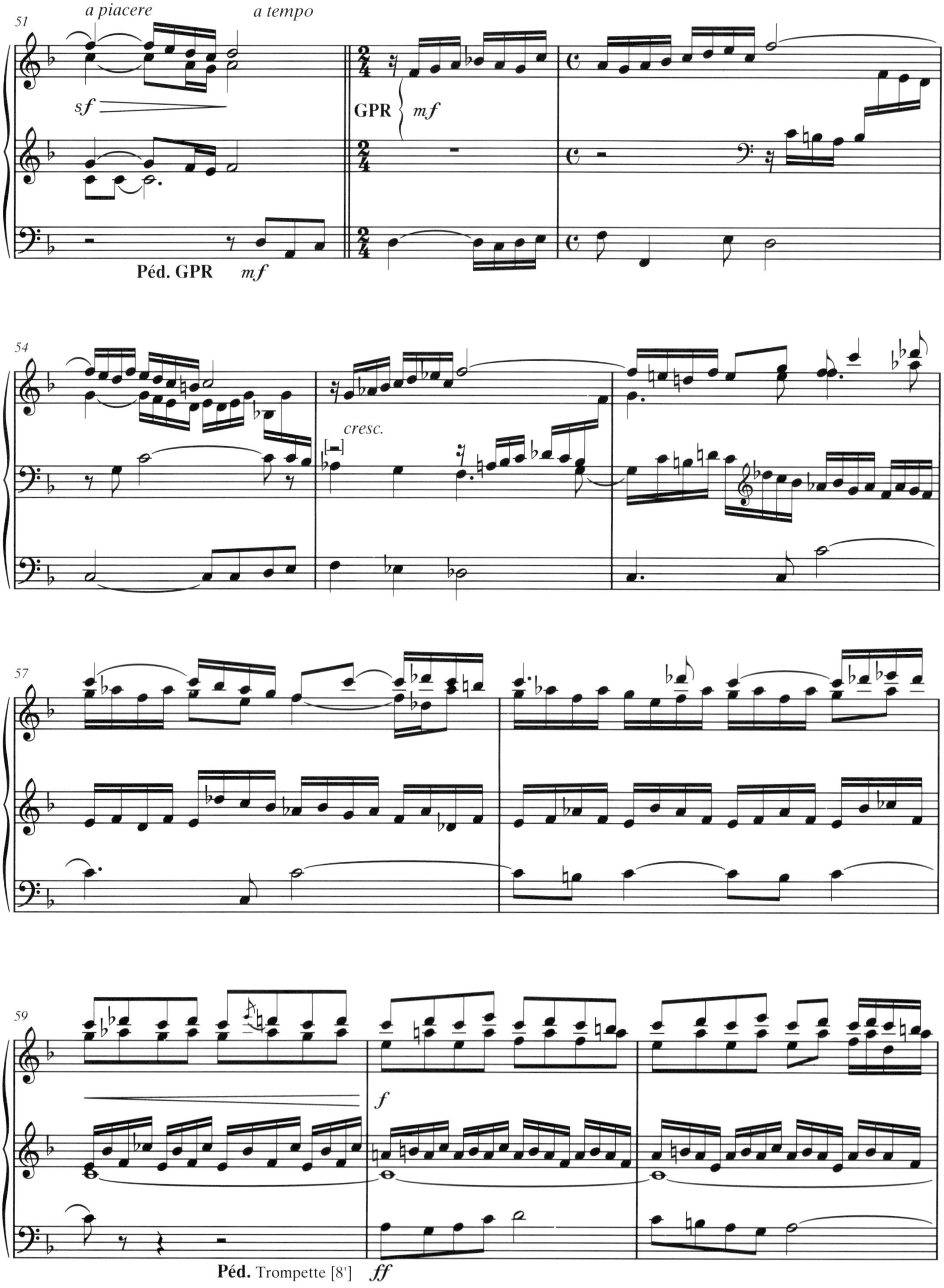
a piacere
a tempo
sf
GPR
mf
Péd. GPR
cresc.
f
Péd. Trompette [8']
ff

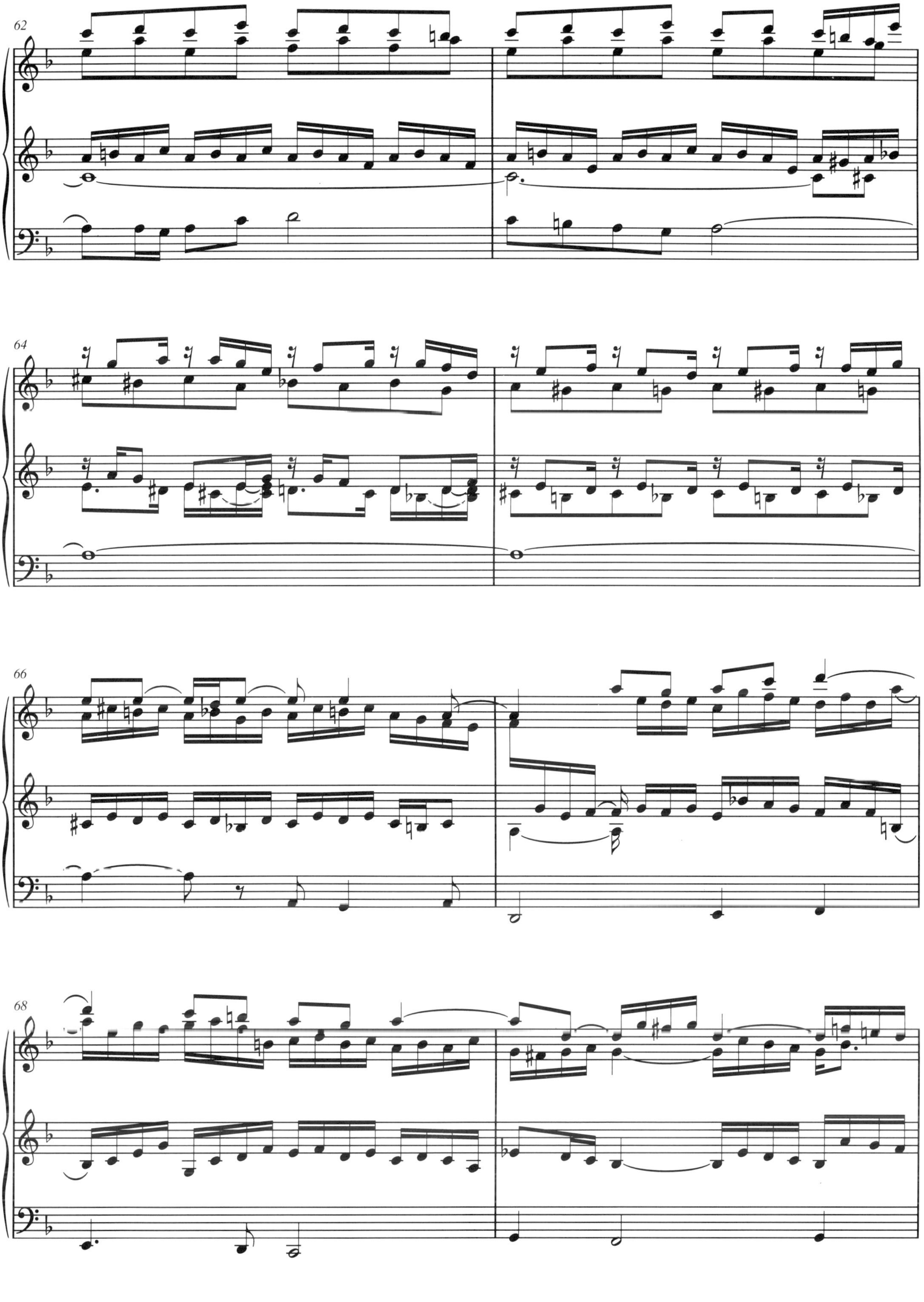
62
64
66
68

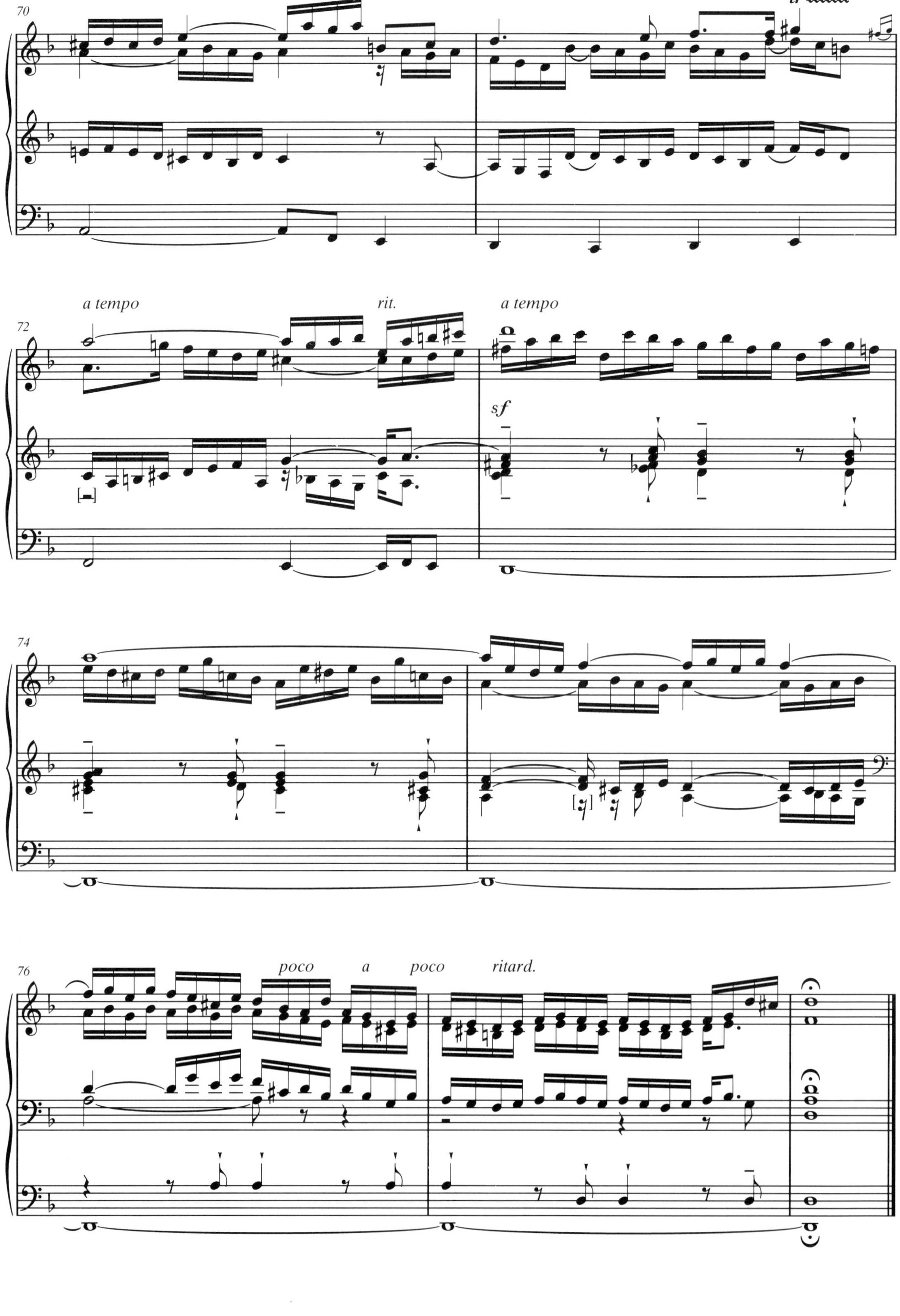
70
rit.
tr
72
a tempo
rit.
a tempo
sf
74
76
poco a poco ritard.

Grand orgue: Flûte 8'
Positif: Fonds 8', 4'
Récit: [Gambe 8'], Voix Céleste
Pédale: Basse 16'

# V. Adagio

17
a piacere
[a tempo]
p
Péd. GPR
21
P
f
P
f
25
a piacere
a tempo
R
p
pp
Péd. R
29
a piacere
a tempo
pp

33

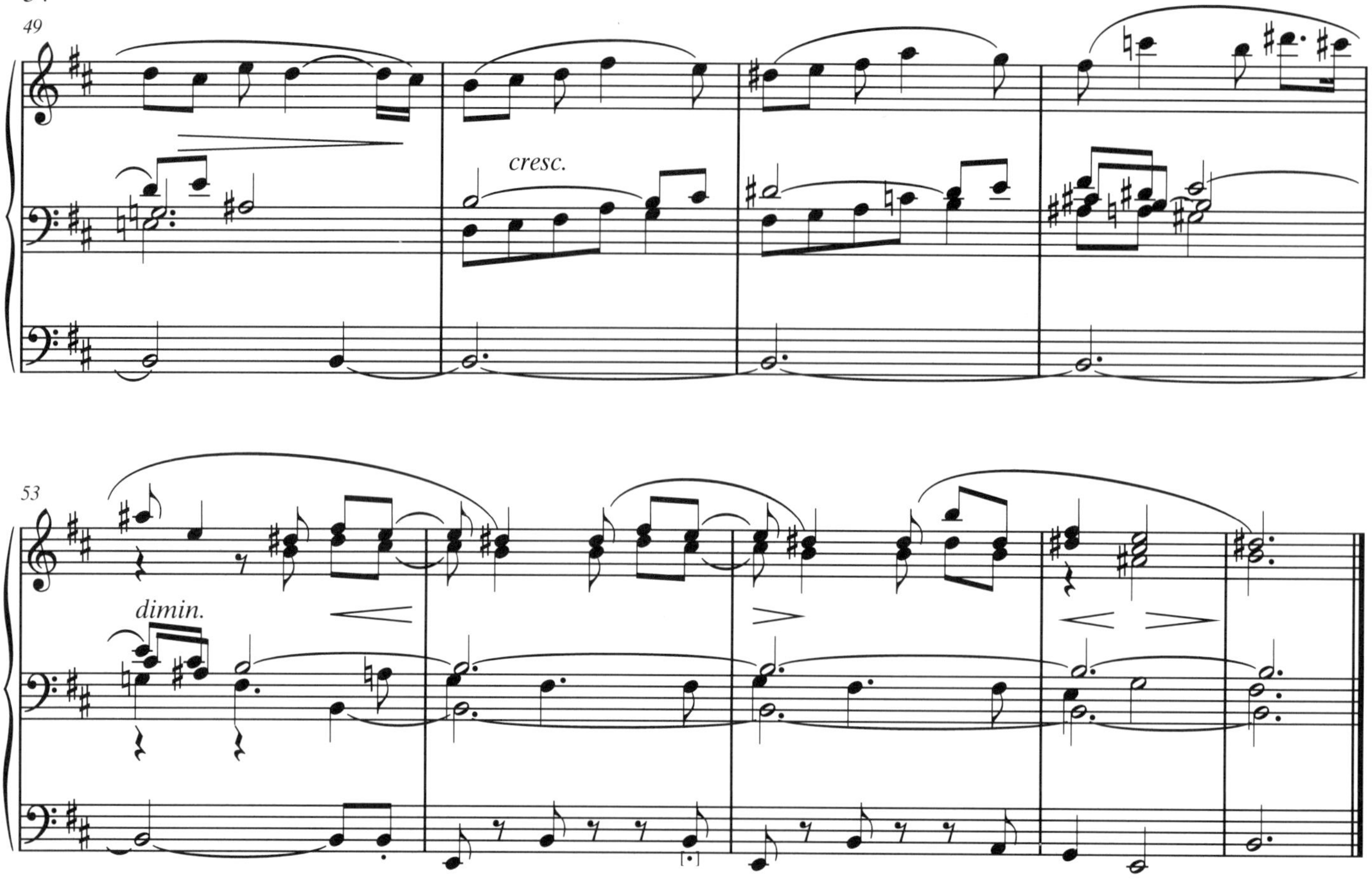
49
cresc.
53
dimin.

# VI. Finale

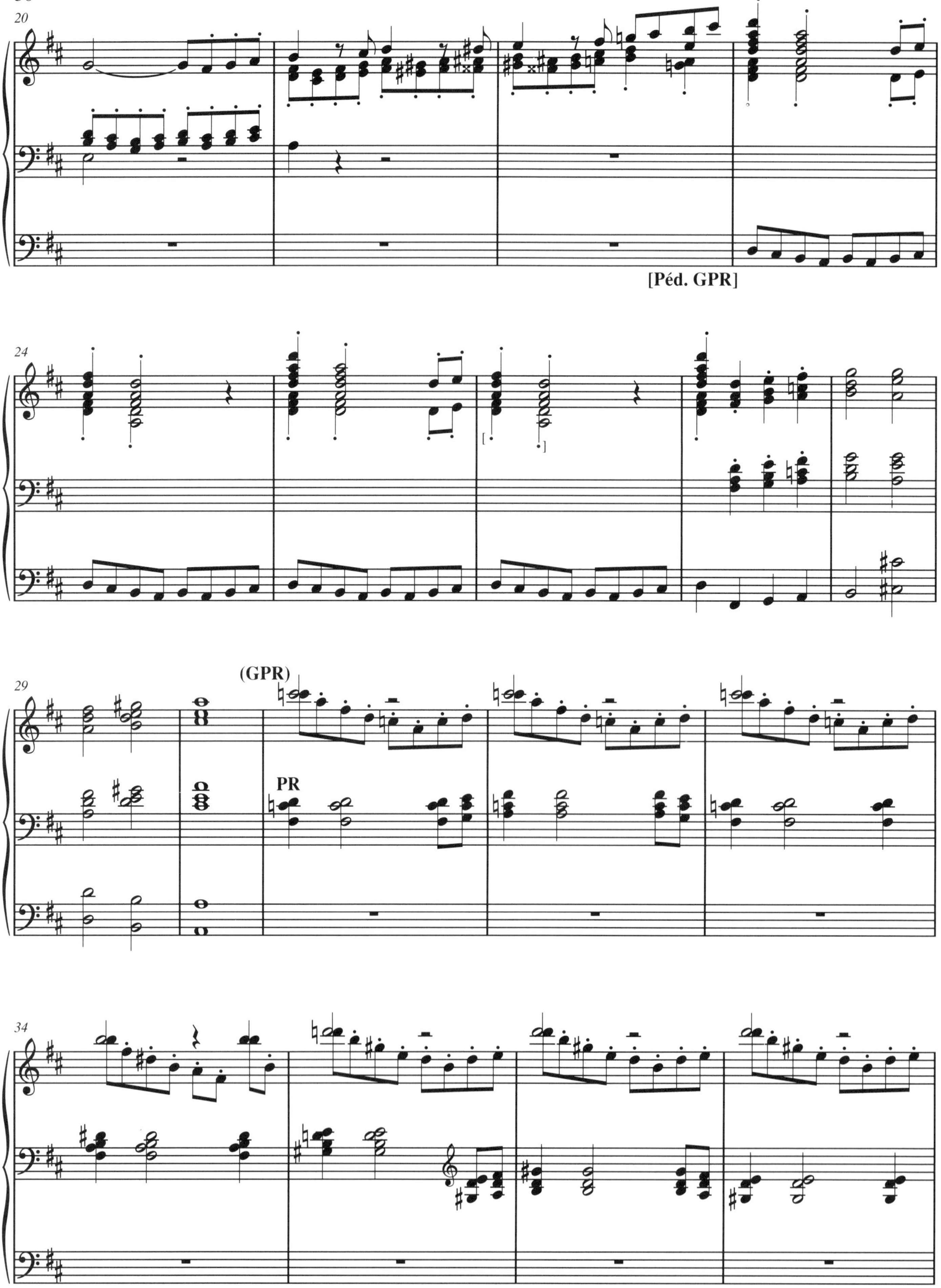
[Péd. GPR]
(GPR)
PR

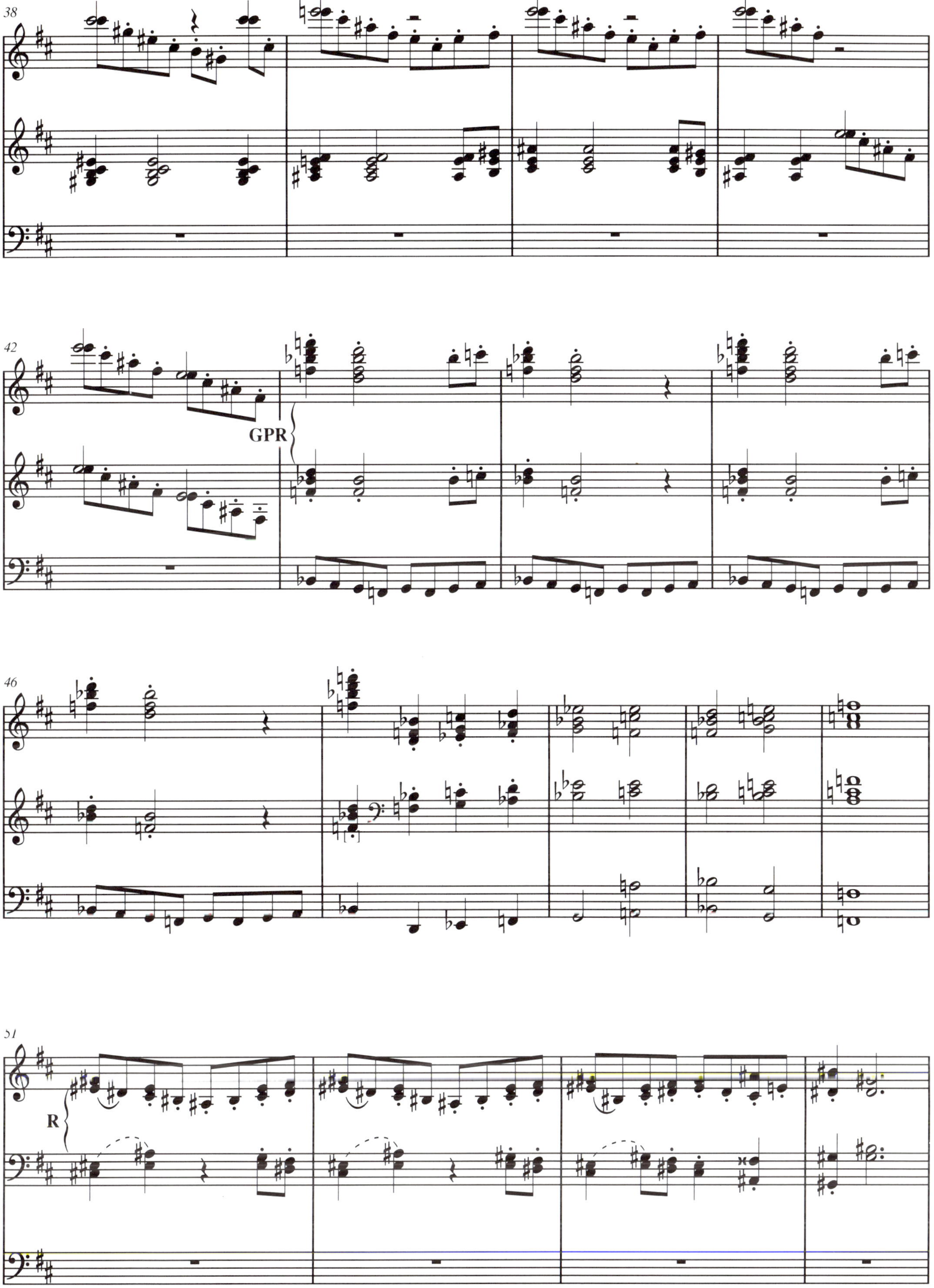
38
42
GPR
46
51
R

38

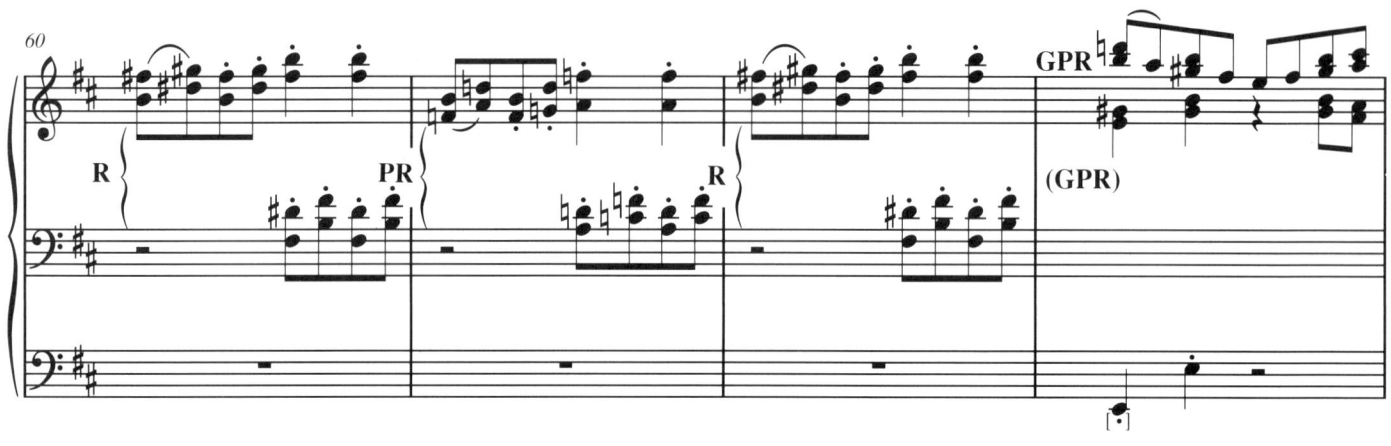

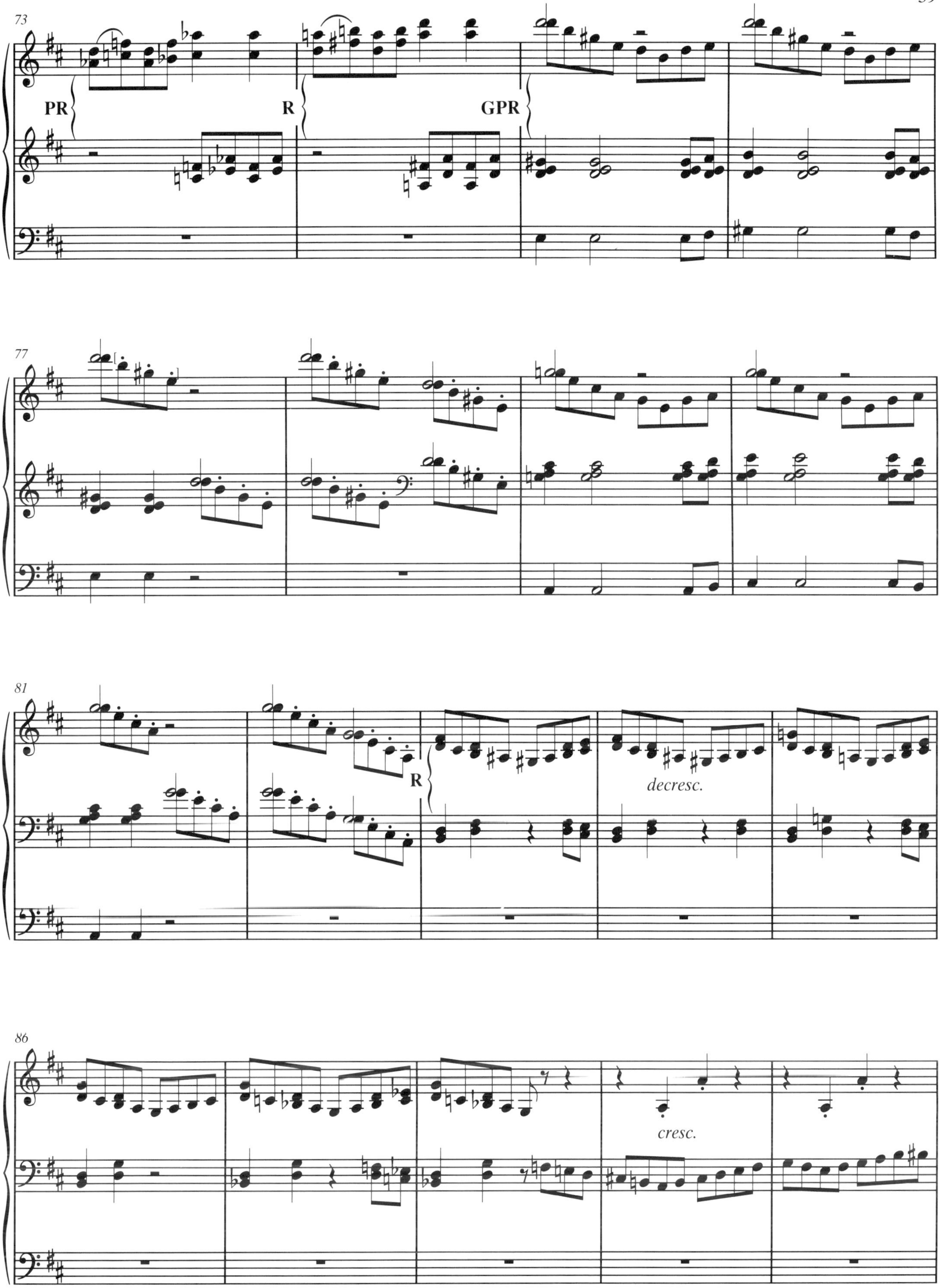
73
PR
R
GPR
77
81
R
decresc.
86
cresc.

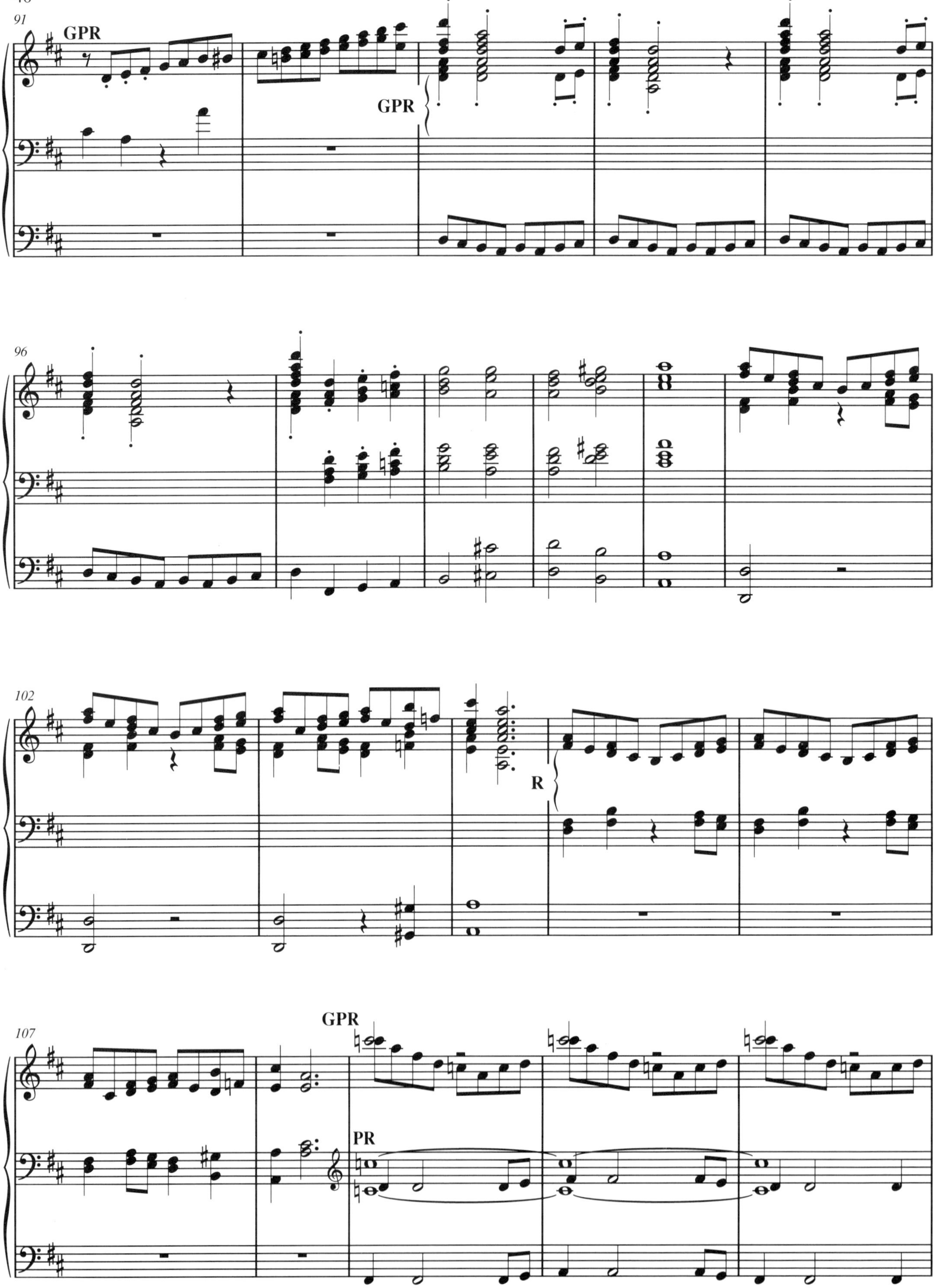
91
GPR
GPR
96
102
R
107
GPR
PR

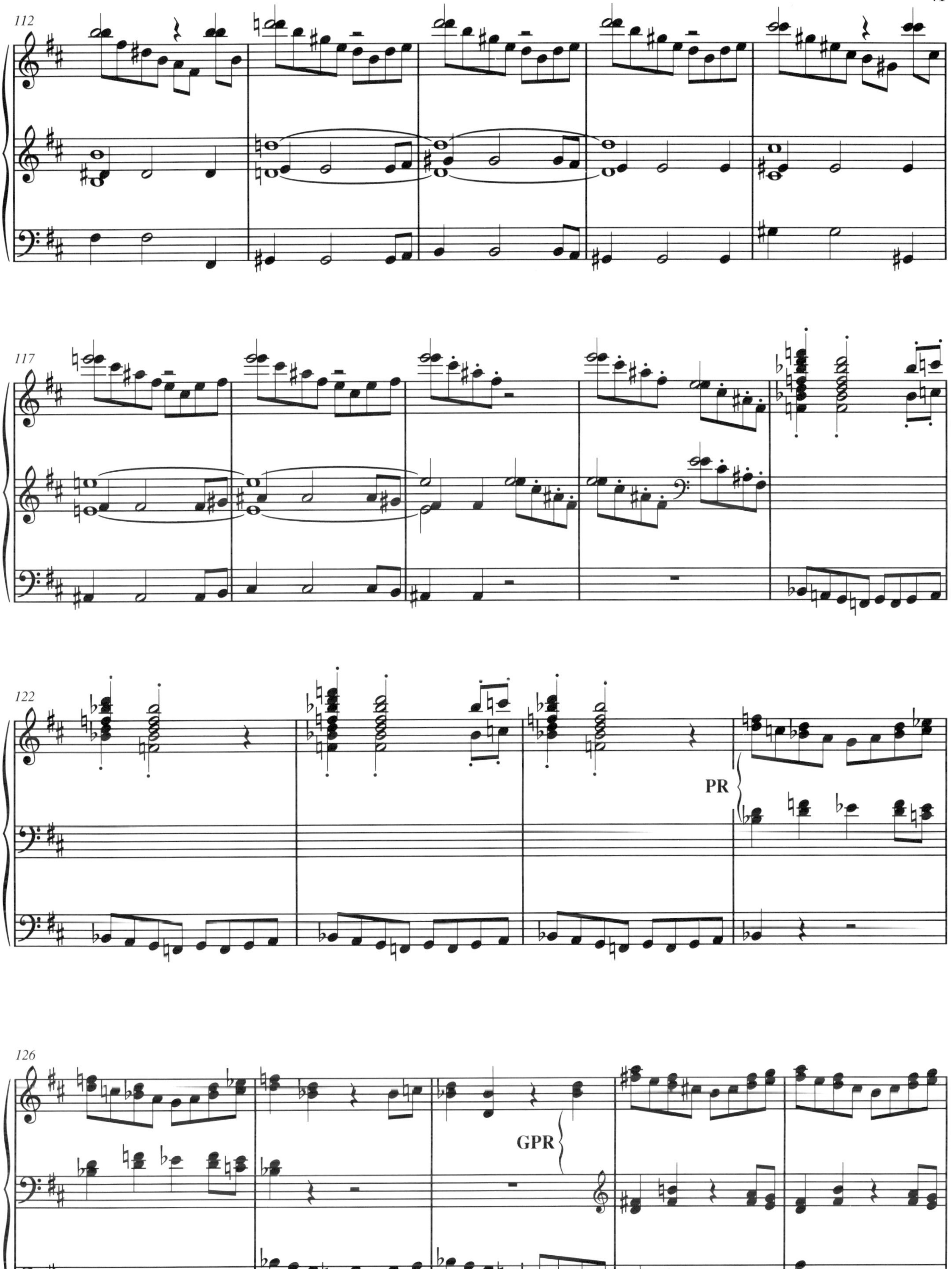
112
117
122
PR
126
GPR

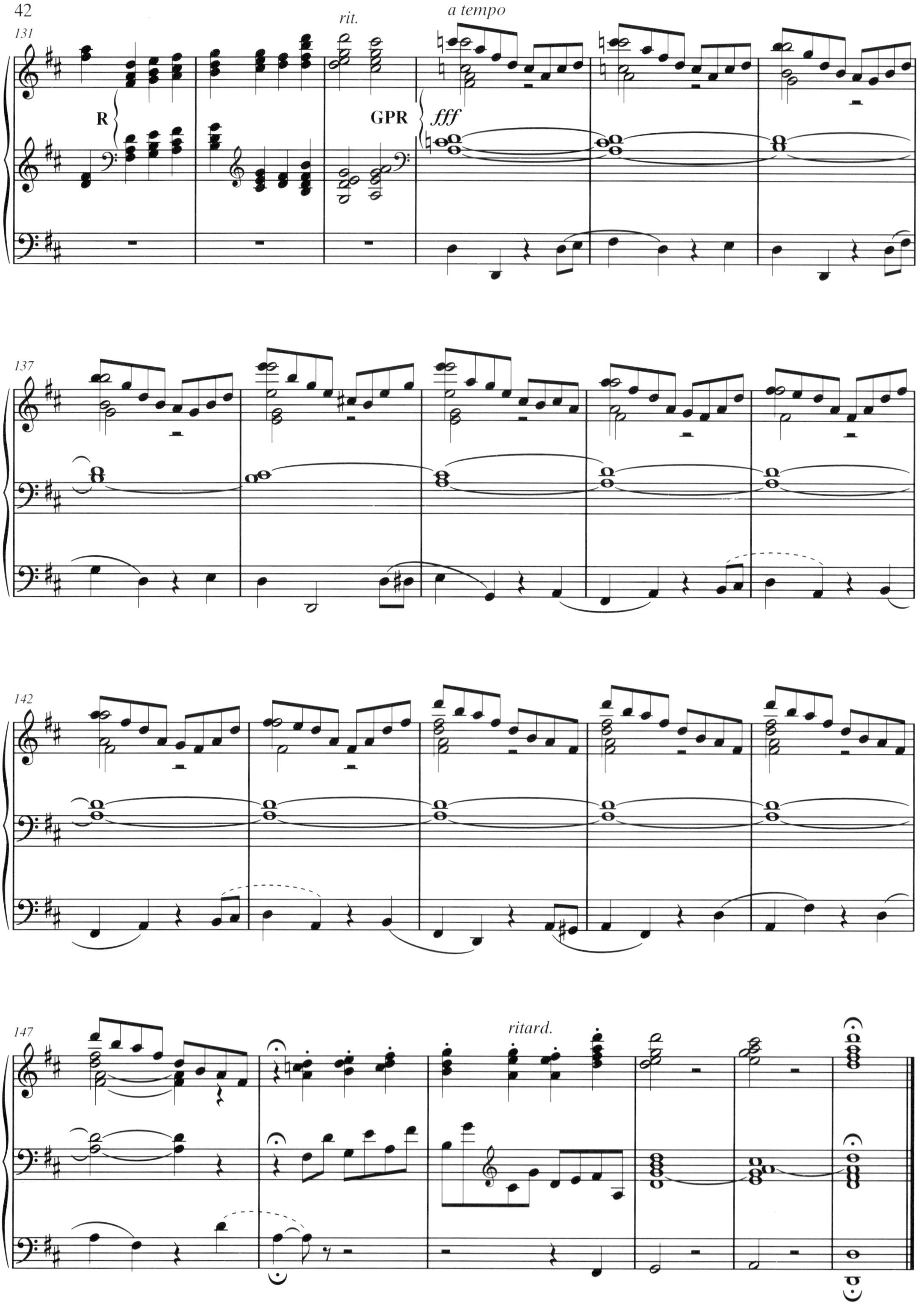
131
rit.
a tempo
R
GPR
fff
137
142
147
ritard.

Appendix 1

# [I] Prélude

Version *A/A′*

Claviers: Fonds 8'
Pédale: Fonds 16', 8'

Clav. 1

**Andantino**

44

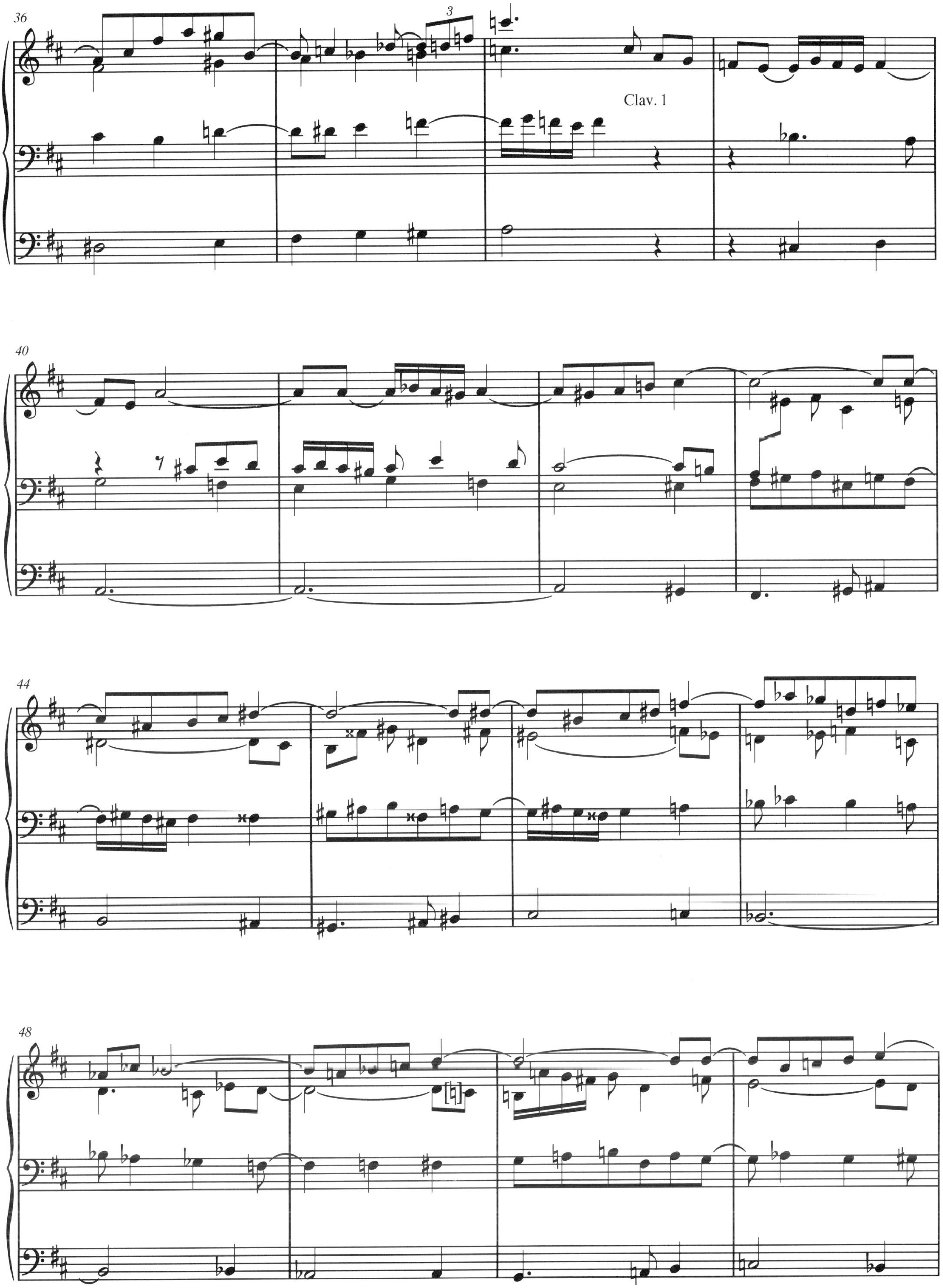
36
3
Clav. 1
40
44
48

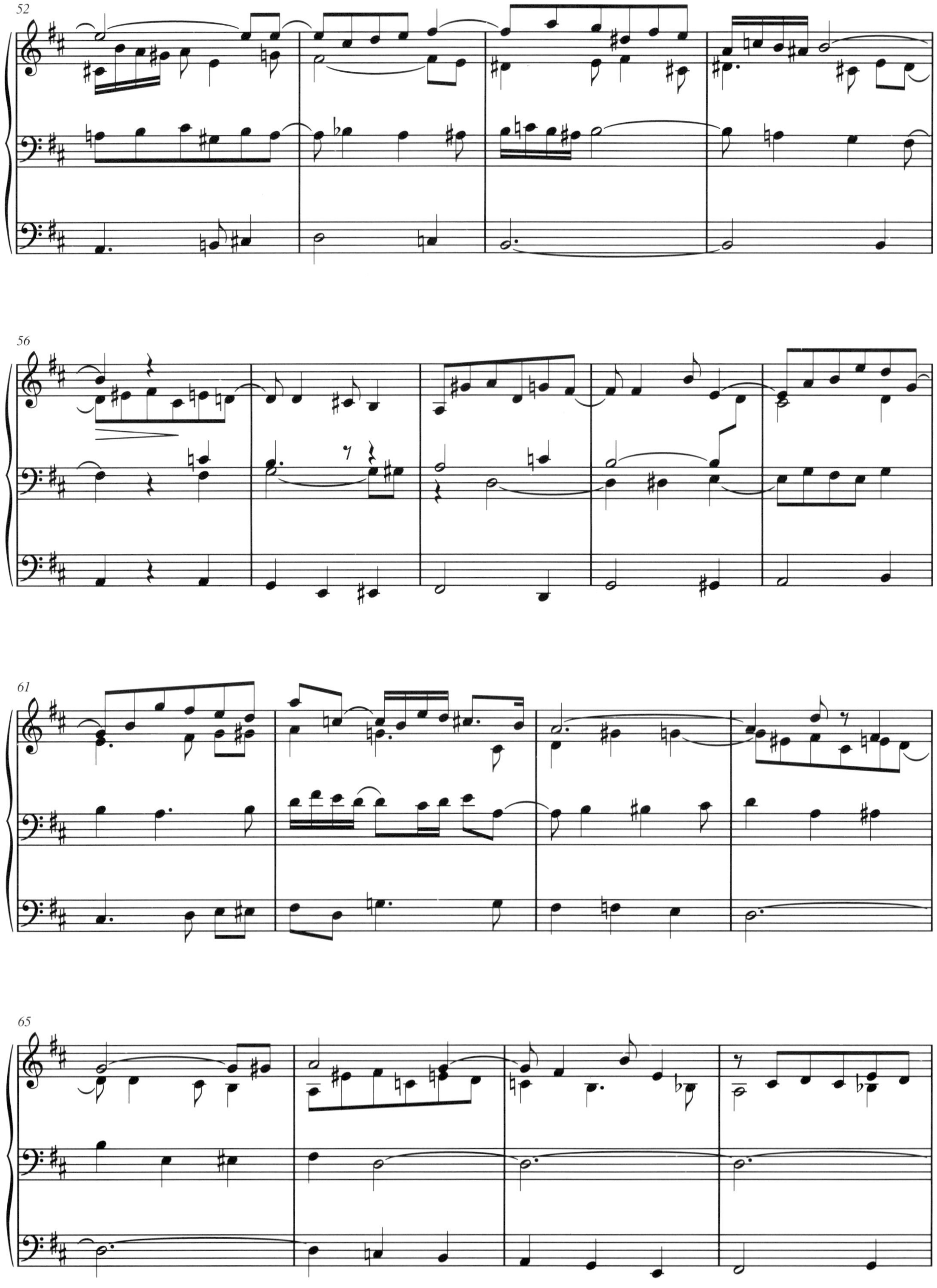
52
56
61
65

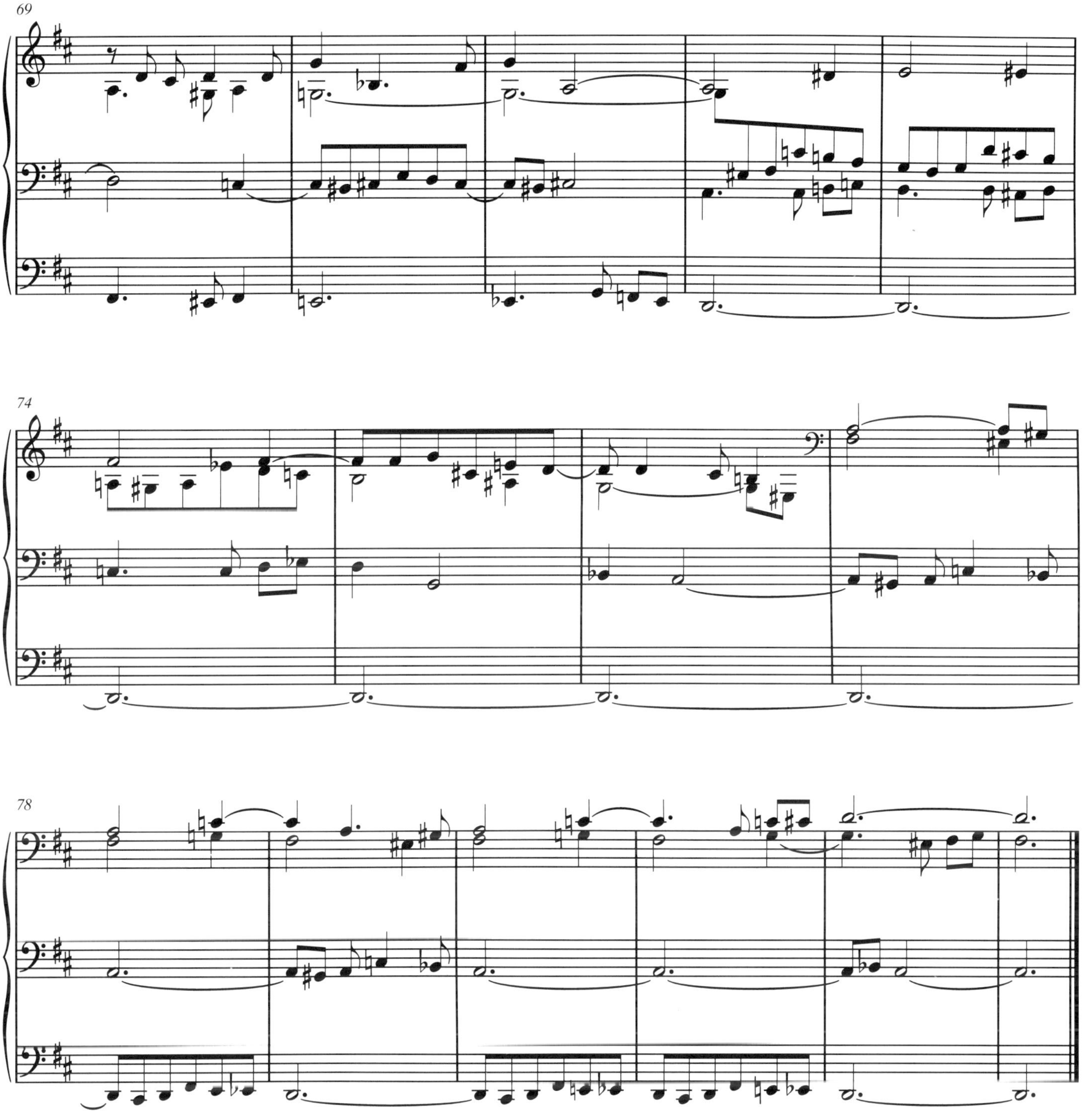
69
74
78

# Appendix 2
# I. Prélude

Version *B/B'*, Mm. 19–28, 54–100

[Mm. 19–28]*

[Mm. 54–100]**

*Version *B/B'*, m. 19 = version *A/A'*, m. 19; version *B/B'*, m. 28 = version *A/A'*, m. 28.
**Version *B/B'*, m. 54 = version *A/A'*, m. 54.

49

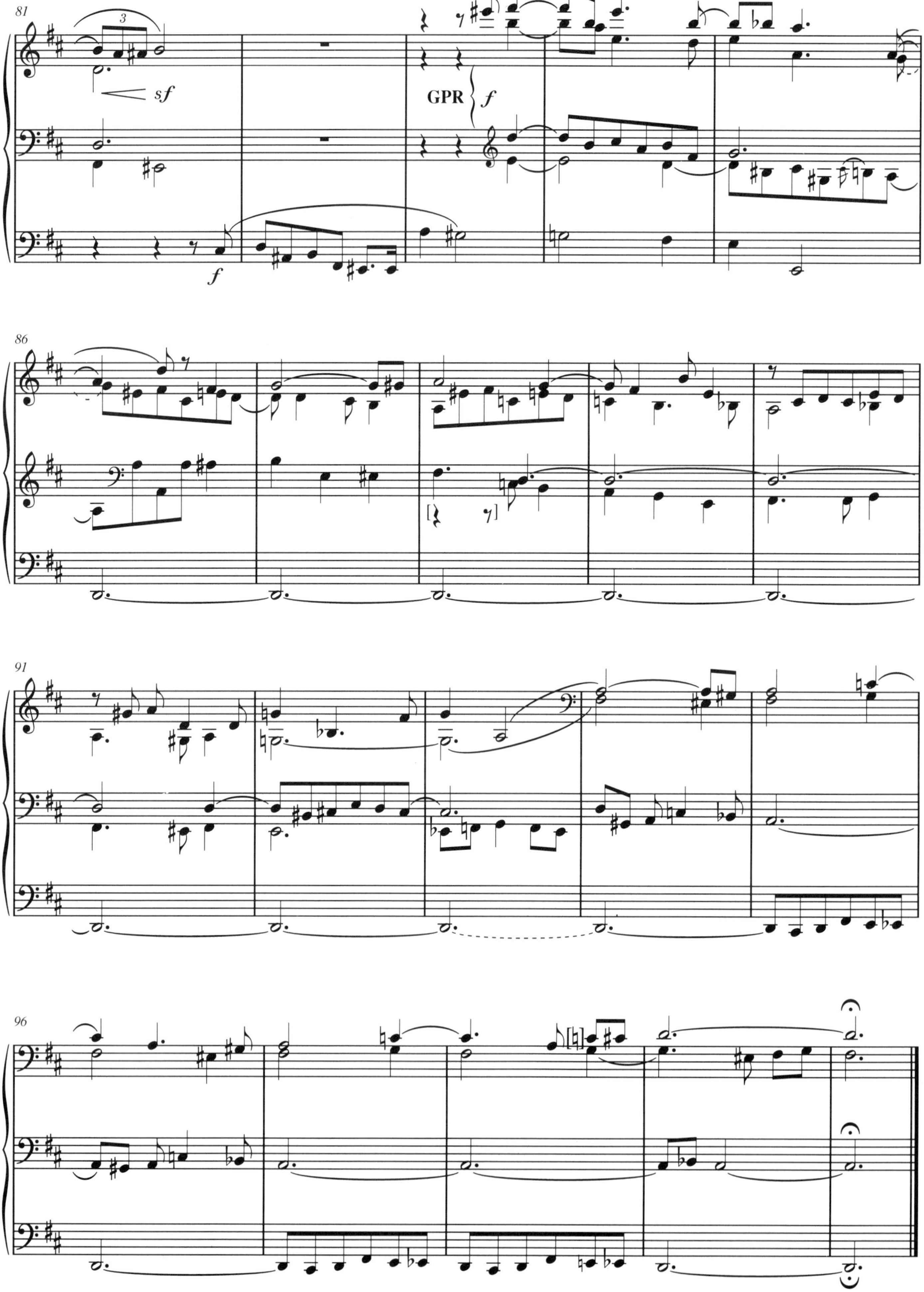
81
3
sf
GPR
f
f
86
91
96

# Appendix 3

## III

Grand orgue: Fonds 8'
Positif: Flûte 8'
Récit: [Gambes 8',] Voix célestes
Pédale: Fonds 16', 8'

Versions *A'/B/B'* and *C/C'*, Mm. 1–44*

*Version *A'/B/B'*, m. 44, and version *C/C'*, m. 44 = version *D/E*, m. 37.

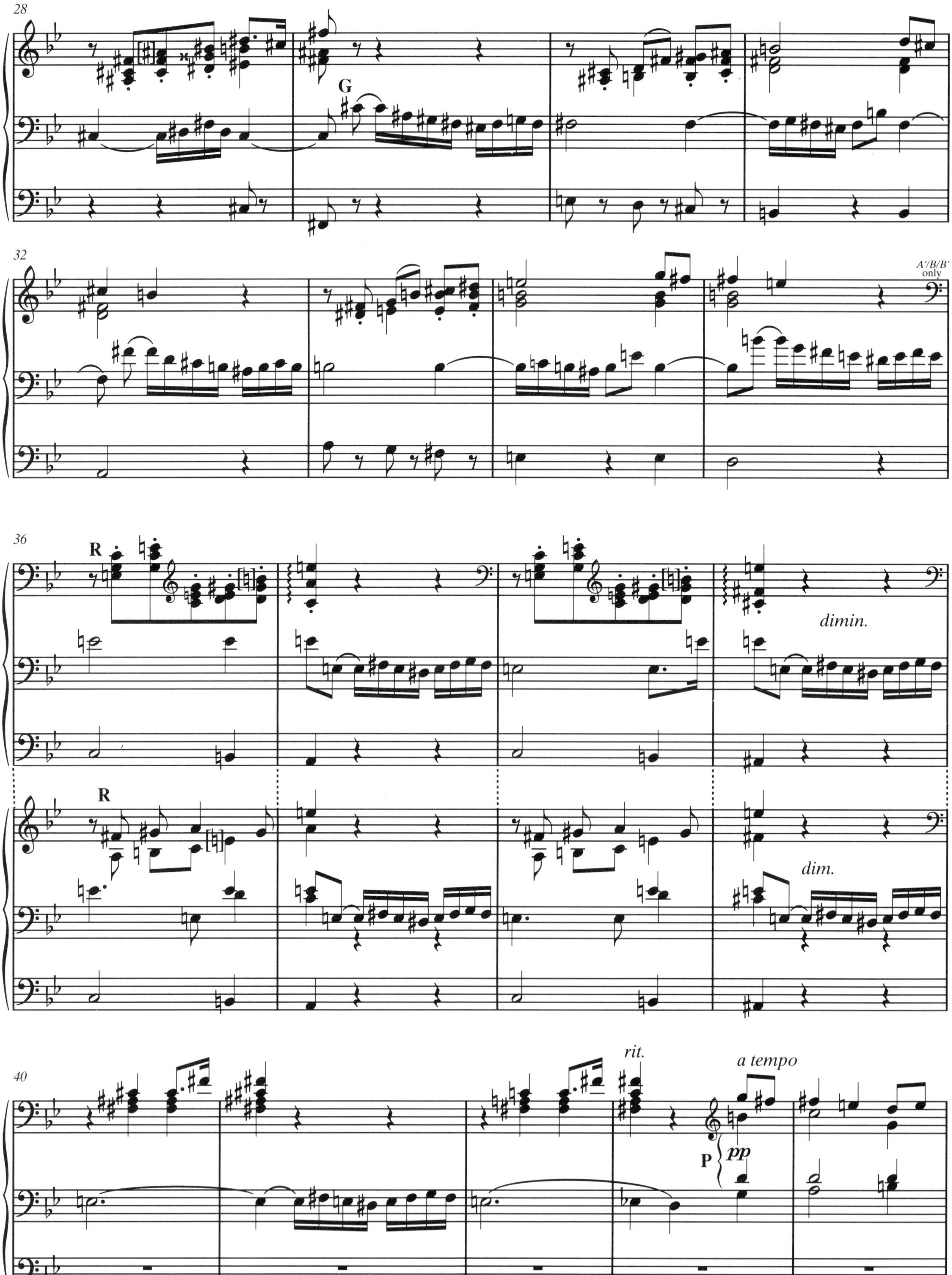
28
G
32
A'/B/B' only
36
R
A'/B/B'
dimin.
R
C/C'
dim.
40
rit.
a tempo
P
pp

… = 112)

# Appendix 4
# IV. Scherzo

Version *A/A'/B/B'*

Grand orgue:
Positif: } Anches 8', 4'
Récit:
Pédale: Fonds 16', Anches 8', 4'

**Allegro** (♩. = 112)

*staccato sempre*

GPR

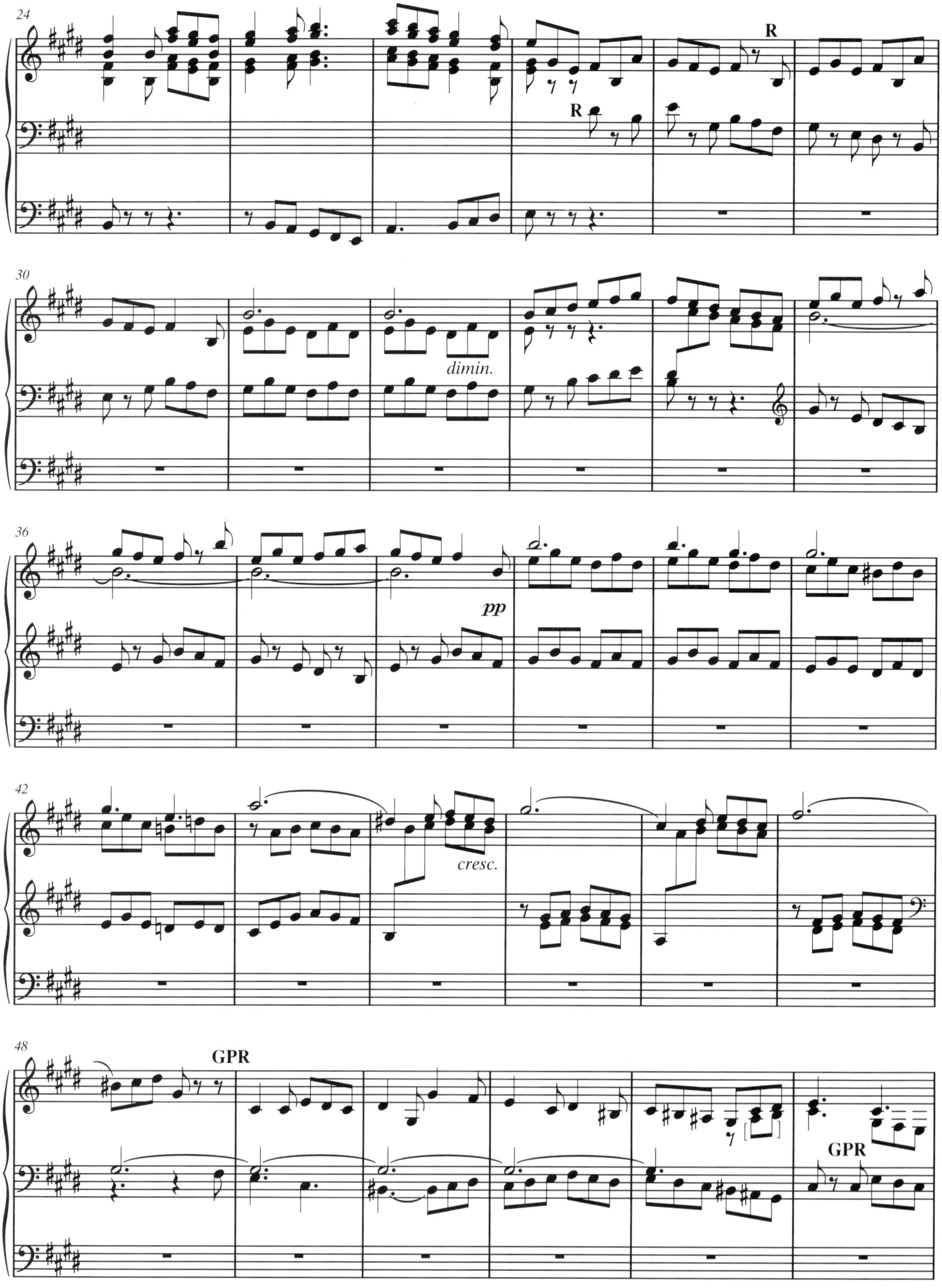
24
R
R
30
dimin.
36
pp
42
cresc.
48
GPR
GPR

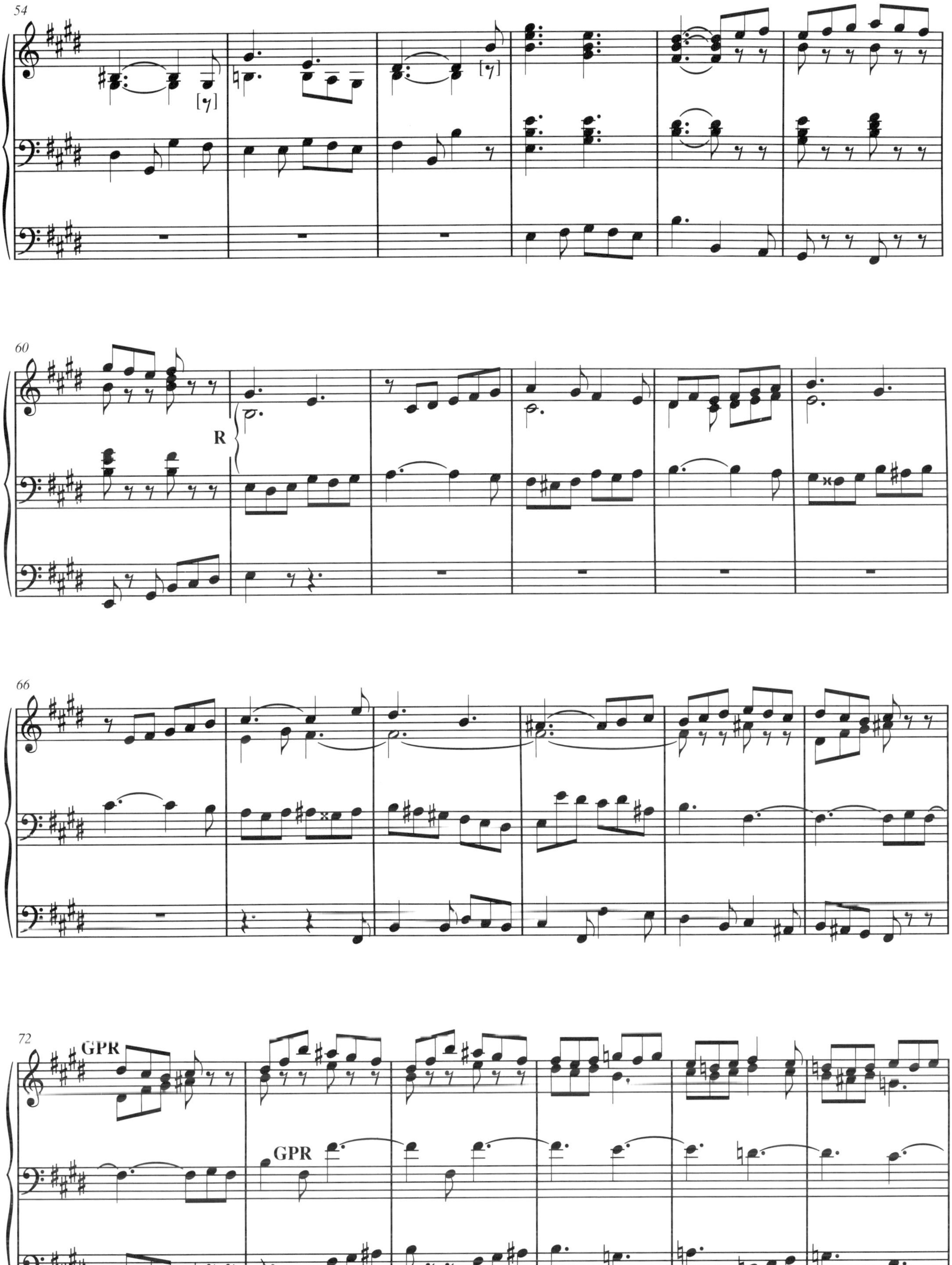
54
60
R
66
72
GPR
GPR

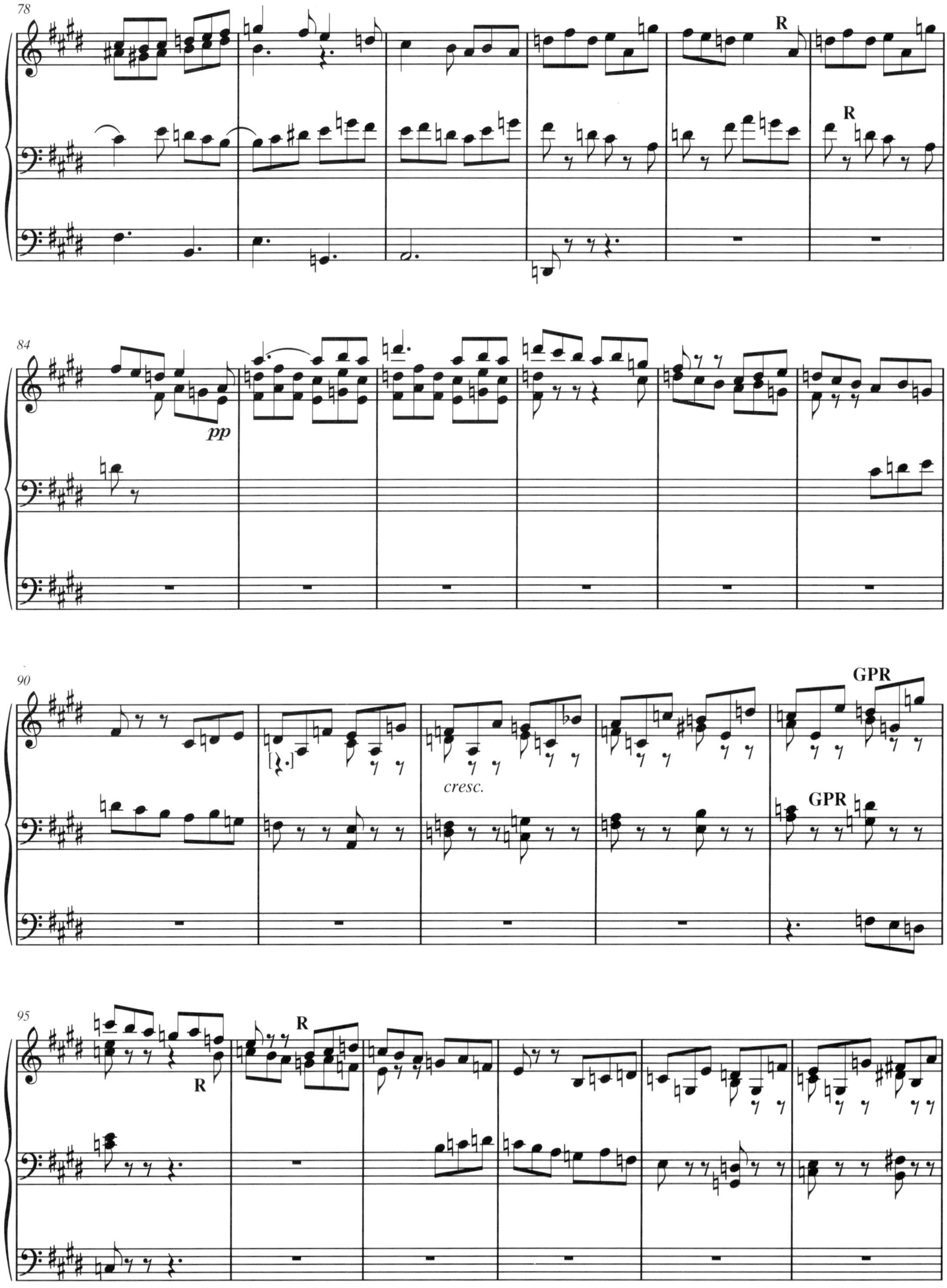
78
R
R
84
pp
90
cresc.
GPR
GPR
95
R
R

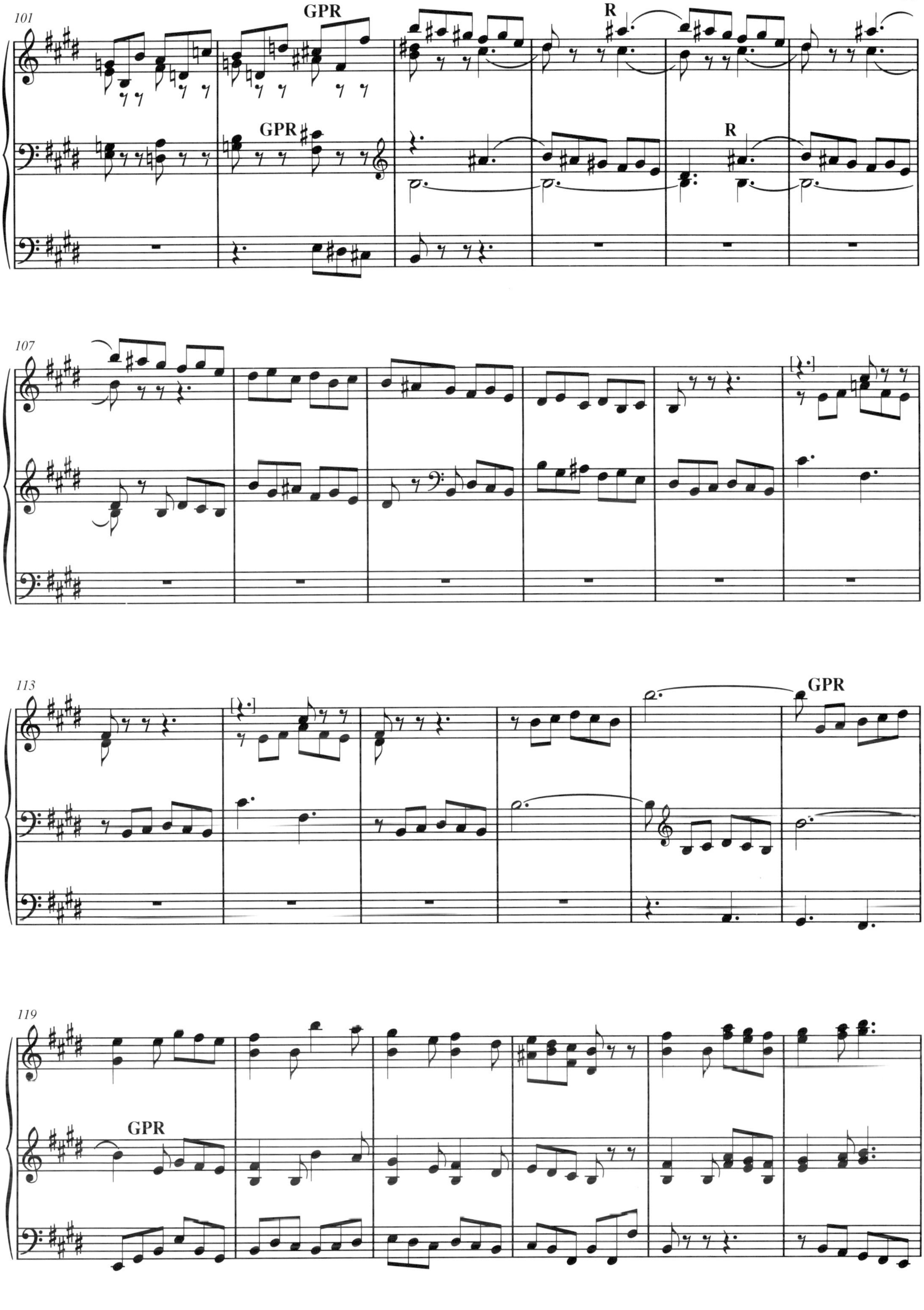
101
GPR
GPR
R
R
107
113
GPR
119
GPR

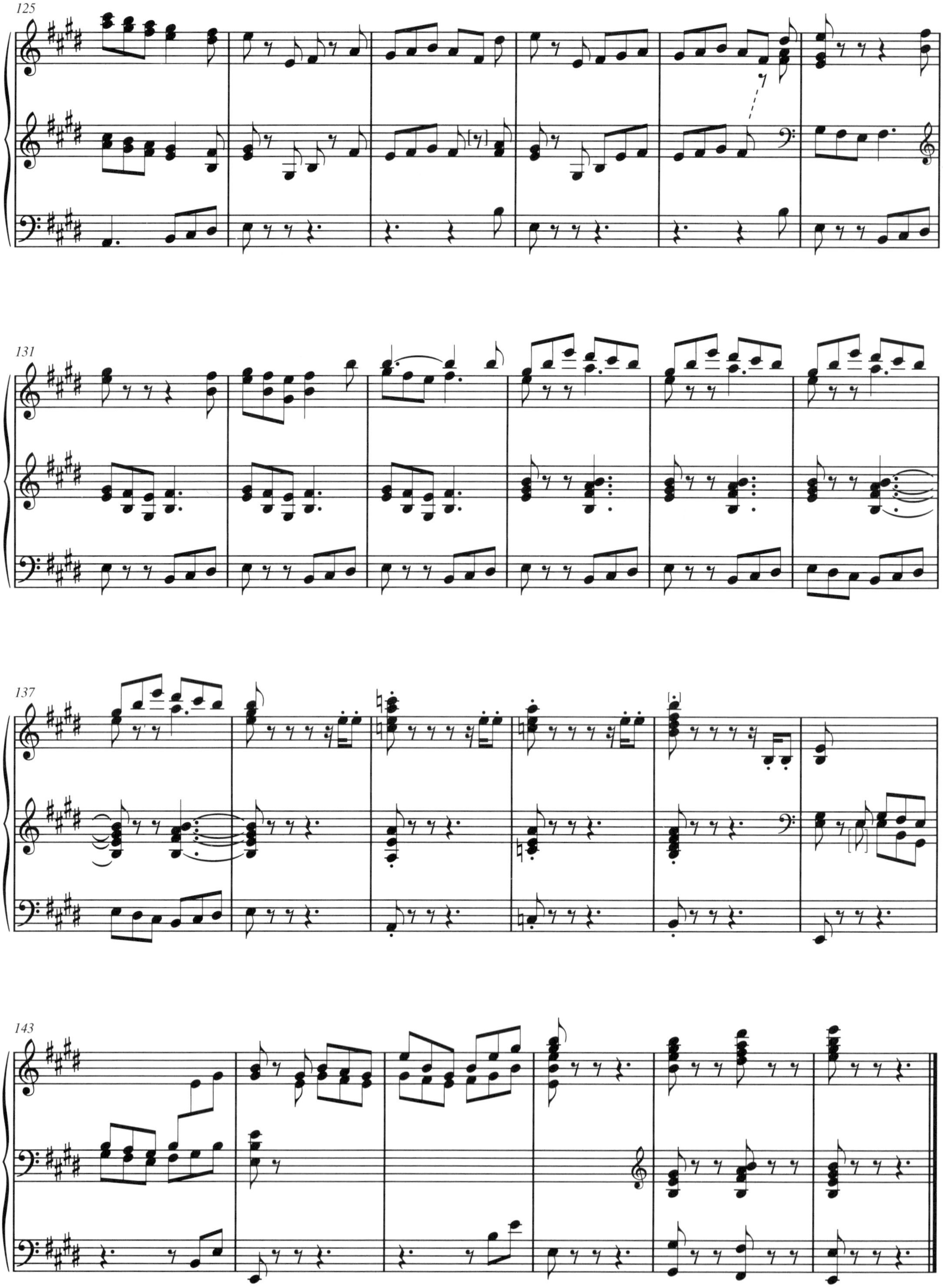
125
131
137
143

Appendix 5

# [V] Adagio

Version *A/A′*

Clavier: Voix humaines [tremblant]
Pédale: Basses 16', 8'

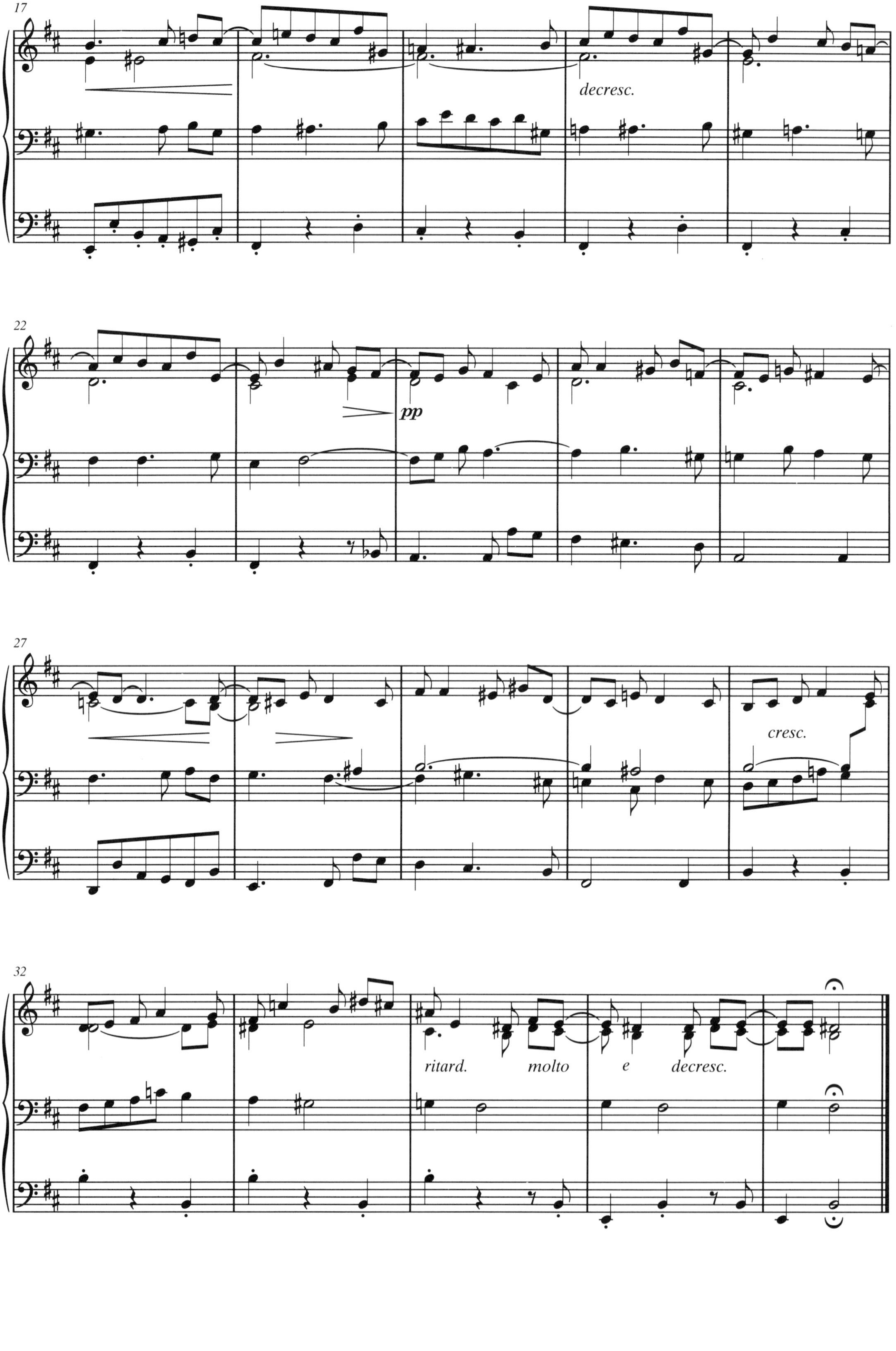
17
decresc.
22
pp
27
cresc.
32
ritard.
molto
e
decresc.

M2.R23834 v.12 Q
  Widor, Charles Marie, 1844-1937.
    Symphonie II.

M2.R23834 v.12 Q
  Widor, Charles Marie, 1844-1937.
    Symphonie II.